50

Targets for the
Mid-Sized Telescope

John A. Read

www.facebook.com/50ThingstoSeewithaSmallTelescope

Final copy edits, formatting, and eBook design by Kurtis Anstey

Cover Image "Hubble Peers into the Storm." Original image by ESA/Hubble. Mild color alternations (to improve text visibility) by Steven J. Catizone. The original image file can be found here: https://www.nasa.gov/sites/default/files/thumbnails/image/potw1636a.jpg

Cover images of the following telescopes provided compliments of Celestron and Sky-Watcher:

Celestron 127EQ PowerSeeker Telescope, Celestron Omni XLT 102, Sky-Watcher 8" Collapsible Dobsonian Telescope, Celestron Omni XLT AZ 130mm Newtonian

Cover image of the Explore Scientific AR102 refractor was taken by the author

Images of finders were provided with permission by the following:
Rigel Quikfinder: Permission compliments of Rigel Systems
High Point Multi-Reticle Red Dot Finder: Permission compliments of High Point Scientific
Telrad photo permission pending

Telescope view source files for deep-sky objects were constructed from actual photos taken by the author, either using his personal four-inch refractor, twelve inch Dobsonian and eight-inch Dobsonian, or using the following remote observatories: Abbey Ridge Observatory (owned by Dave Lane) and the Burke-Gaffney Observatory at Saint Mary's University, Halifax. These images were then processed to simulate a visual observation, and then (in almost all cases) inverted to improve visibility when using this book in the dark.

Star maps used in this book were sourced using Stellarium, an open-source stargazing program. These maps were then customized using various software programs for the purpose of this book. Stellarium is the best astronomy software out there (and it's free). A link to this software can be found here: http://stellarium.org

Images from NASA follow NASA's photo usage guidelines found here:
http://www.nasa.gov/audience/formedia/features/MP_Photo_Guidelines.html

The book is dedicated to Isaac and Oliver

May you dream of the stars, and reach for the Moon

Note from the author

Written as a follow up to *50 Things to See with a Small Telescope*, containing virtually no overlap in content, *50 Targets for the Mid-Sized Telescope* introduces the beginner stargazer to a new assortment of astronomical wonders. With easy-to-follow star maps, that are unique for each target, the budding astronomer will explore the Universe like never before.

Each target has been carefully chosen to be observable in telescopes with apertures between four and eight inches. Most objects can be viewed from the suburbs, in mildly light polluted conditions, with only a few noted exceptions that require darker skies. On dark, moonless nights, most targets will be visible in small telescopes, and binoculars, too.

M42 Photographed with my four inch Explore Scientific Refractor

CONTENTS

Acknowledgements

I'd like to thank all of the people directly involved in the production of this book. Dave Chapman, five-time editor of the *Royal Astronomical Society of Canada's Observer's Handbook*, completed a major content edit (while vacationing in Costa Rica). Dave's guidance significantly increased the usability of this guide. Dr. Luigi Gallo (my astrophysics professor at Saint Mary's University) thoroughly reviewed the manuscript for scientific accuracy. Without his review, I may have accidently stated that stars rise in the west. Several early edits of this book were completed by my wonderful (and very patient) wife, Jennifer Read. Final cover design was completed by the very talented Steven J. Catizone (who created the covers for my science fiction series, too).

I'd like to thank the Halifax Centre of the Royal Astronomical Society of Canada for hosting the 2016 Nova East Star Party. At this event, a third of the book's images were captured while young stargazers watched in awe as the pictures appeared on my telescope's camera screen.

A huge thanks to Dave Lane from Saint Mary's University. With the support of the University, Dave created the first (and second) Twitter-operated remote observatories. His personal observatory, Abbey Ridge, and the university's Burke Gaffney Observatory were used to make several of the "telescope view" images that make this book so handy.

I'd also like to thank the Mount Diablo Astronomical Society, and the Carolina Skygazers. These two organizations nurtured my love for astronomy, leading me to leave Corporate America and pursue my passion for astrophysics in academia.

And special thanks to the NASA Night Sky Network and the Astronomical Society of the Pacific, for enabling thousands of events and reaching millions of students around the world. If it weren't for your network, this book would not have been possible.

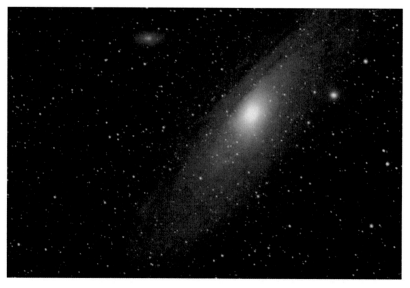

A 60-second exposure of M31, captured at NESP as young stargazers counted down the exposure (10! 9! 8!), and then 'oohed' and 'aahed' as the image appeared on the laptop.

Tips and Tricks

So, you've just set up your new mid-sized telescope, and it's time to look at some stars! There are a few things you'll want to consider before you can expect to see some of the dimmer targets, like galaxies, nebulae, and globular clusters.

The most important thing to do when attempting to observe the objects listed in this book is to adapt your eyes to the dark. It takes at least twenty minutes for your eyes to adjust for the purpose of viewing these deep-sky objects. Think of your eyes as a stopwatch: every time you look at a light, the twenty-minute clock resets.

Dim deep-sky objects, like galaxies, require extremely dark skies to be observed

If you're in the suburbs, make sure you ask your neighbors to turn off their porch lights. Don't look at your cell phone or a computer screen. These reset your eyes' clock, too. Avoid flashlights at stargazing events. Red lights are usually okay, but should be used sparingly.

Don't even look at the Moon, or any bright stars, through your telescope before attempting to view a deep-sky object, such as a galaxy or nebula. There is only one exception to this rule. If your goal is to observe the Moon, or double stars, then you don't need to worry about adapting your eyes to the dark.

Have patience. Even with years of experience using a telescope, it still takes me several minutes, and sometimes longer, to find the deep-sky object I'm looking for. Sometimes, factors like light pollution and Moon phase make it impossible to see the dimmer objects, and you'll just have to try another night. This happens all the time in astronomy. Failed attempts are part of the hobby.

Try to set up your telescope on solid ground. Avoid setting it up on decks or wooden structures. On wood, the subtle movement of your body will translate into vibrations visible through your eyepiece.

The most effective way to become proficient in amateur astronomy is to get involved. Almost every city in North America has an astronomy club. Members are a wealth of knowledge in nearly every aspect of astronomy. And while attending club meetings you get to meet some amazing speakers. At our local club, we recently had David Levy speak. Levy was one of the people credited with discovering comet Shoemaker–Levy 9, which crashed into Jupiter in 1994; an event witnessed by stargazers around the globe.

To find the astronomy club nearest you, please visit:
http://nightsky.jpl.nasa.gov (USA)
www.rasc.ca/locations-across-canada (Canada)
www.skyandtelescope.com/astronomy-clubs-organizations/ (All)

Accelerate Your Exploration!

If you want to find astronomical objects quickly and easily, I highly recommend one inexpensive upgrade. Instead of a finder scope, your primary star-finding tool should be a unit-power finder. Unit-power finders provide a reference point in the sky *without* magnification, making it easy to match the sky to your star chart.

The Telrad is the heartiest of the unit-power finders, but is best suited for larger telescopes. It comes with double-sided tape to secure it to your optical tube (I actually drilled holes in my Dobsonian telescope, bolting the device in place). It's also very easy for kids to use (I once used the Telrad for teaching children at a library event how to photograph the planet Jupiter).

Telrad Unit Power Finder

The Rigel QuikFinder is great for mid-sized telescopes, like my 102mm refractor. There isn't enough room on the body of my refractor telescope for a Telrad, but the Rigel QuikFinder fits perfectly. When using the QuikFinder, the eye must be perfectly positioned behind the unit, and this can be a challenge for young children. That being said, I love this finder and highly recommend it.

The Red Dot Finder is the simplest and, in most cases, least expensive option. I've seen several variants of this type of finder online, for as little as $14. The High Point Scientific Red Dot Finder is probably one of the best, and is priced comparable to the Telrad and QuikFinder. The difference is that while the Telrad and QuikFinder display a bullseye on the sky, the Red Dot Finder only displays a red dot.

Rigel QuikFinder Compact Reflex Sight

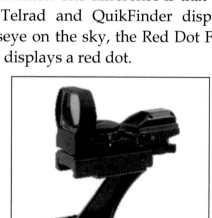

*High Point Scientific
Red Dot Finder*

Why keep your finder scope?

Finder scopes allows you to see dim stars that are invisible to the human eye. This is especially helpful in the city where light pollution clouds the view of all but the brightest stars.

Do I Need Astronomy Software?

The maps in this book provide sufficient guidance to find all 50 objects. This is because each target (except the Moon) is *outside* the Solar System, and none will significantly change position during a human lifetime. However, if you are using this book in conjunction with *50 Things to See with a Small Telescope,* or are searching for a comet, satellite, etc., you *will* want to use astronomy software.

I use astronomy software primarily when preparing to observe planets, comets, and asteroids (all objects located within the Solar System). A planet's location is difficult to ascertain in a book, because the planet's position changes a little bit each night. This is why it's helpful to check astronomy software as you plan your observing session.

I use a simple program called Stellarium, a program that meets all of my observing needs. You can download the software **for free** at: www.stellarium.org.

It's worth exploring Stellarium's more advanced features (it can even control a go-to telescope). My favorite feature is confirming the position of the moons of Jupiter and Saturn. If you zoom in (by scrolling with your mouse) on a planet like Jupiter, you can see the exact position of its moons as they change position over time.

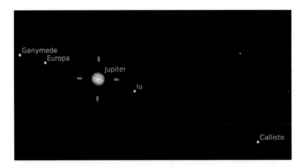

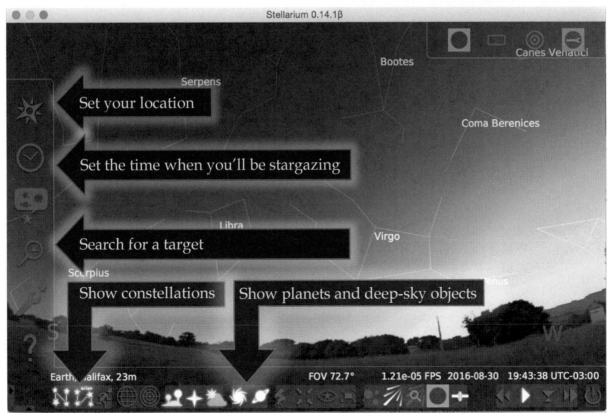

How to use Stellarium

How to Use This Book

50 Targets for the Mid-Sized Telescope features star charts I have edited to show a large portion of sky. In each chart, the most prominent star groupings *for the season* will be clearly visible. Learning to identify these star formations will lead you to the targets in this book.

In the winter sky, most objects will be referenced in relation to Orion, a constellation identified by a row of three bright stars (called Orion's Belt). A bright orange star, Betelgeuse, rests near the top of the constellation, while Rigel, a blue giant star, resides at the bottom. Orion's "sword" contains the Orion Nebula, as described in the book *50 Things to See with a Small Telescope.*

For targets in the northern sky, I'll typically use the Big Dipper as a guide. The Big Dipper can also be used to find the North Star (Polaris). To do this, follow the two stars at the front of the cup (called the Pointer Stars) over to the next brightest star.

Orion

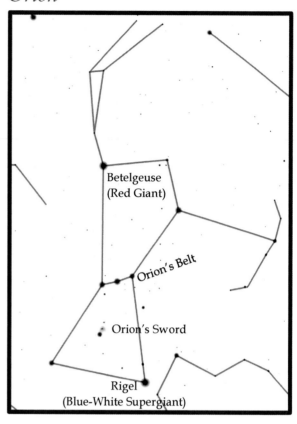

Betelgeuse
(Red Giant)

Orion's Belt

Orion's Sword

Rigel
(Blue-White Supergiant)

Cool Trivia: The North Star is the 48th brightest star in the sky!

The Big Dipper, Arc to Arcturus, and the North Star

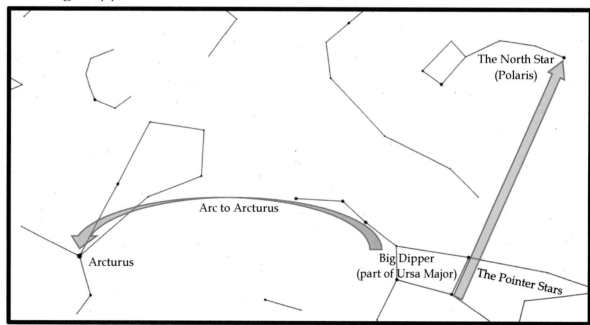

The North Star
(Polaris)

Arc to Arcturus

Arcturus

Big Dipper
(part of Ursa Major)

The Pointer Stars

The Teapot and the Rake

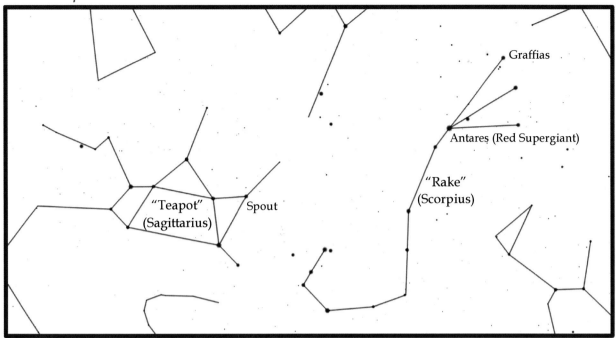

In summer, most targets will be found in reference to the "Rake" (Scorpius), and the "Teapot" (a pattern within the constellation Sagittarius). Scorpius is easy to identify as a large claw or rake. Note that from northern locations, Scorpius never rises far above the horizon.

Higher in the sky, the Summer Triangle will be your guide to dozens of objects. The triangle is formed by three stars: Vega, Deneb, and Altair. Identify Deneb as the top star in a pattern called the Northern Cross. Vega lies above a dim diamond of stars, while Altair is flanked by two other semi-bright stars.

The Summer Triangle and the Northern Cross

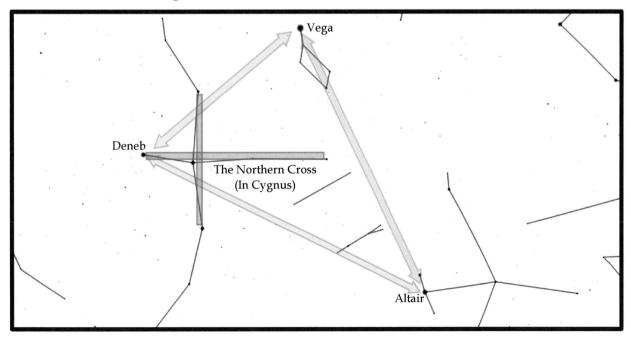

Finding Leo

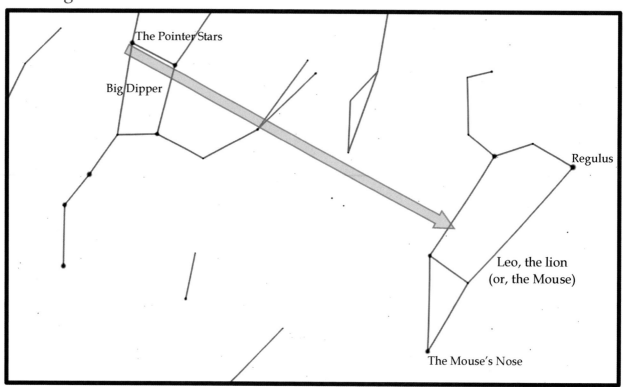

In the spring, we'll use Leo, the lion (which I think looks like a mouse). Leo can be found by following the pointer stars (used to find the North Star) in the opposite direction. The brightest star in Leo is Regulus. Several fall targets will use Cassiopeia, known as the Big W.

In the early fall, Cassiopeia is in the northeastern sky, to the right of the North Star. Once you know what to look for, the Big W is hard to miss. During the winter, Cassiopeia will rise over the North Star and proceed into the northwestern sky, taking on the appearance of a compression bow.

Finding Cassiopeia (the Big W)

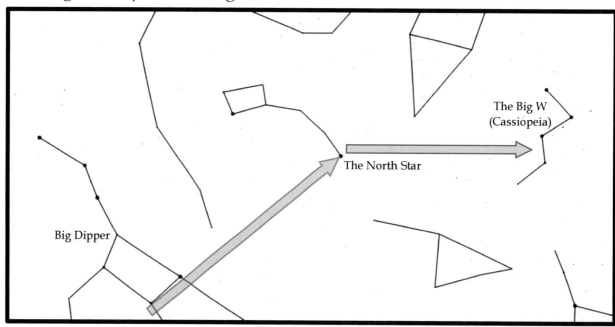

Appreciating the Night Sky

There are copious objects to see in the sky, and I often forget which targets I've observed. That's why astronomy clubs (as well as teachers and scientists) recommend you record your observations. Melody Hamilton of the Royal Astronomical Society of Canada has a phrase she repeats over and over: "Put your observations down on paper!"

In the year 1610, Galileo sketched Saturn's rings and Jupiter's moons. Looking at these sketches hundreds of years later, we gain insight into how he perceived the skies. By putting your observations down on paper, you begin with a simple look through a telescope, and suddenly, you're doing science! You create a permanent record, a history that can be referenced years later. These recordings provide insight into your process as an amateur astronomer.

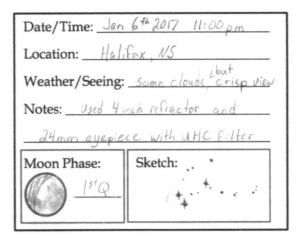

Date/Time: Jan 6th 2017 11:00 pm

Location: Halifax, NS

Weather/Seeing: Some clouds but crisp view

Notes: Used 4 inch refractor and 24mm eyepiece with UHC filter

Moon Phase: 1st Q

Sketch:

For this reason, I've included a place on every page for you to record your observations. In this box, be sure to record how clear the sky appears (this is called "seeing", in astronomy), as well as what type of telescope you are using (some telescopes mirror-reverse the image, and this may affect your drawing). Don't forget to shade in the phase of the moon.

Reading the Star Maps

Each map in *50 Targets for the Mid-Sized Telescope* has been created to show only the information required to find your target. No more, and no less. Most of the charts follow a two-step process.

Targets in this book are organized by season, but if you're observing early in the evening you may be able to see lingering targets from the previous season. And, if you stay up late, you may be able to find items from the next!

Step 1: Locate reference stars using one of the prominent star groupings mentioned earlier. Follow these stars along the BLUE arrow.

Step 2: Use the reference star to narrow in on the target. The ORANGE arrow will point precisely at the object we are attempting to observe.

(Easy targets will only contain step 2)

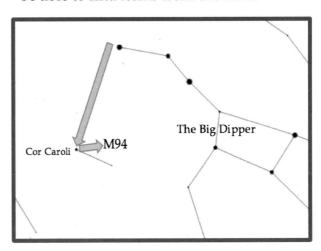

Cor Caroli • → M94

The Big Dipper

1. The Lunar X

Dave Chapman, editor of the *RASC Observer's Handbook*, was thumbing through Moon photos on my phone when he paused, zooming in on one of the images. "You got it!" he said, looking surprised. "Got what?" I responded. "You've got the Lunar X!" I looked at the image. On the screen shone a perfect X in a font like the logo for the company *Space X*!

Also known as the "Werner X," named for the nearest crater, the Lunar X is a visual phenomenon induced by sunlight and shadows interacting with the lunar topography. Timing is key to this observation, since the X pattern only occurs for a few hours each month.

The X appears around the time of the Moon's first quarter (less than a week after the crescent moon). It's impossible to observe the event every month, because, clouds aside, sometimes it occurs when the Moon is on the other side of the Earth.

There is a science to predicting when the X will appear, involving spreadsheets detailing "peak X", "partial X," and so

| Date/Time: _____ |
| Location: _____ |
| Weather/Seeing: _____ |
| Notes: _____ |

Moon Phase: _____ | Sketch:

on. I believe the best way to catch the phenomenon is simply to observe the Moon during every first quarter phase.

Each night the Moon's shadow patterns change and there are many other interesting phenomena to observe; but the Lunar X is definitely one of the best.

First Quarter Moon   *Crescent Moon – About four days earlier*

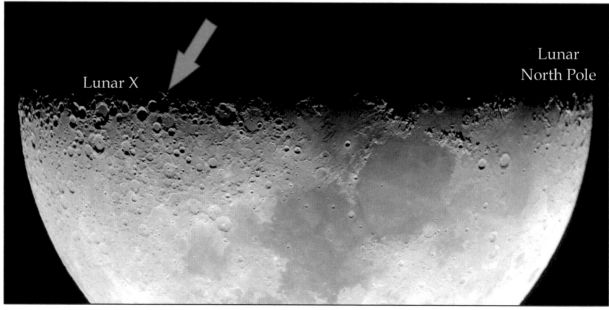

Lunar X

Lunar North Pole

Photo of the Lunar X taken with the author's iPhone, through a telescope.

WINTER

Despite reluctance to drag a telescope out into the cold, winter is often regarded as the best stargazing time of the year. The sky darkens around 6 p.m., and the air is crisp, granting sharp views through telescopes free from dew. Popular deep-sky objects, like the Great Nebula in Orion (M42), are high in the sky. For many, winter summons the "first light" of a new telescope unwrapped from under a tree. The new year welcomes an abundance of objects waiting to be explored, but thanks to short days and long winter nights, many autumn targets can still be seen before they sink below the western horizon.

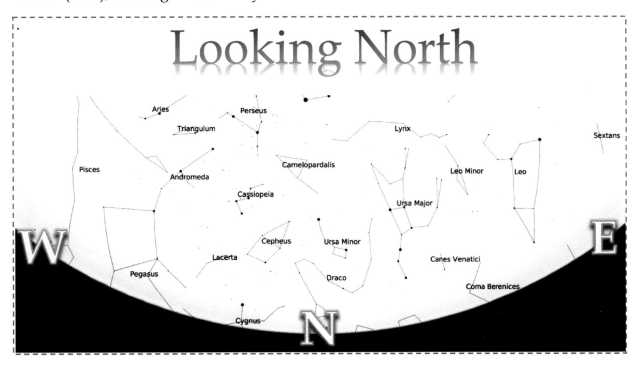

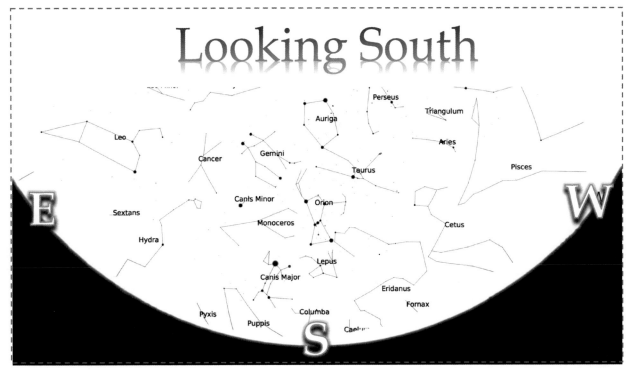

2. The Trapezium (Theta Orionis)

In *50 Things to See with a Small Telescope,* we explored the finest nebula in the night sky, The Orion Nebula (M42). With a small telescope the Orion Nebula's shape is definitely visible, but with a mid-sized telescope, we get to explore it!

In the center of the Orion Nebula lies a grouping of stars called the Trapezium (the central stars form a trapezoid).

The Orion Nebula is the easiest nebula to find and can be seen without the aid of a telescope, in the "sword" below Orion's belt. If you're having trouble finding it, use the bright orange star Betelgeuse, and follow a line down though the left star in Orion's belt.

| Date/Time: _____ |
| Location: _____ |
| Weather/Seeing: _____ |
| Notes: _____ |
| _____ |

Moon Phase: _____

Sketch:

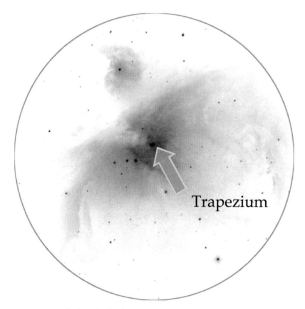

Trapezium

Orion Nebula (M42) through a telescope

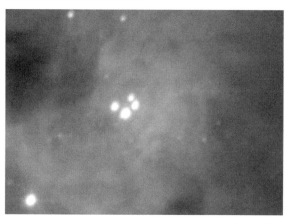

A closer look at the Trapezium

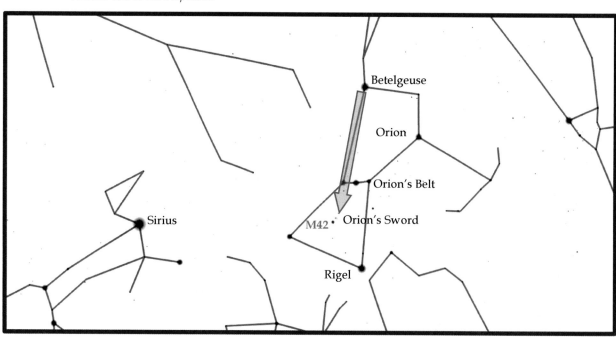

Betelgeuse

Orion

Orion's Belt

Sirius

M42   Orion's Sword

Rigel

3. Sigma Orionis

You've probably seen the photos of the Horsehead Nebula taken from the Hubble Space Telescope, that dark stallion riding on a red sea. Unfortunately, for the amateur, the Horsehead is incredibly difficult to see visually, even with large telescopes. Images of the Horsehead are typically derived from CCD cameras fitted with special filters.

However, the star system that illuminates the red sea where the stallion rides is called Sigma Orionis, and it's a beauty! To me, the cluster of stars surrounding Sigma Orionis resembles a medieval sword, which is fitting since the cluster resides just below Orion's belt.

Date/Time: _____

Location: _____

Weather/Seeing: _____

Notes: _____

_____

Moon Phase: _____

Sketch:

WINTER

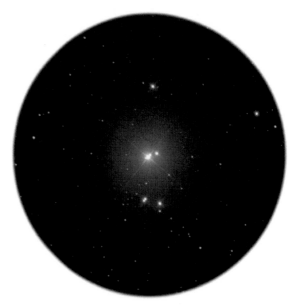
The Sigma Orionis Cluster (Rotated)

Close-up view of Sigma Orionis

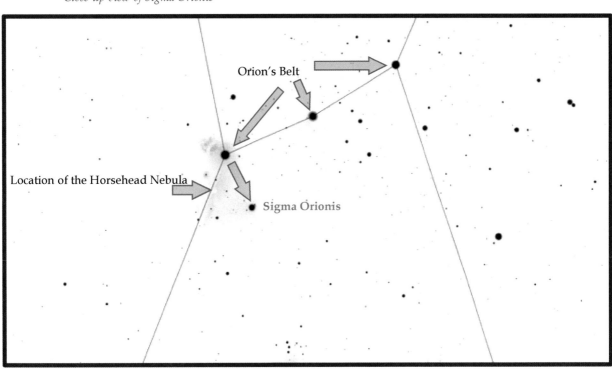

Orion's Belt

Location of the Horsehead Nebula

Sigma Orionis

4. Winter Alberio

This may be the most underrated double star in the sky. I've volunteered at hundreds of events with my astronomy club in California, and not once did Winter Alberio (also known as 145 Canis Majoris) come up as a target.

This pair of stars is arguably one of the most beautiful doubles, mainly due to the contrasting colors, which some say rivals Alberio, the famous double star at the base of the Northern Cross.

John Herchel (son of the famous astronomer William Herchel who discovered Uranus) cataloged thousands of double stars, recording his observation of Winter Alberio (which is cataloged as H3945[1]), from the Cape of Good Hope in his book *Results of astronomical observations made during the years 1834, 5, 6, 7, 8, at the Cape of Good Hope* (Public Domain).

For those at high northern latitudes (I'm currently observing from Canada), this double star doesn't rise very high, so you may need to use software like Stellarium to determine when it's best to view. Find Winter Alberio by following a line up the hind leg of Canis Major.

| Date/Time: _____ |
| Location: _____ |
| Weather/Seeing: _____ |
| Notes: _____ |

| Moon Phase: | Sketch: |

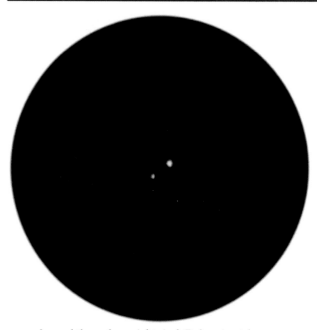

Imaged through an eight- inch Dobsonian telescope

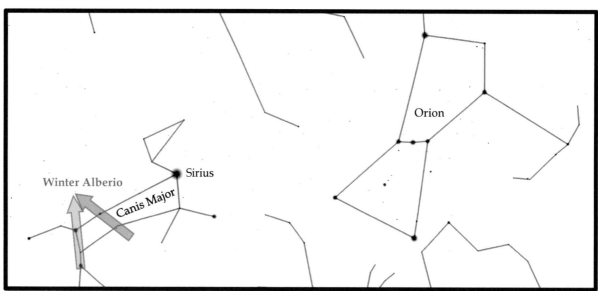

[1] If you have a go-to telescope, this target may be cataloged as SAO 173349

5. Eskimo Nebula (NGC 2392)

Continuing with our wintery theme, there is a very interesting target in the constellation Gemini (The Twins). This planetary nebula is nicknamed the Eskimo Nebula for its resemblance to the fur hoods worn by the Inuit people, who live in the Artic. Be careful with the term, however. "Eskimo" is not politically correct when used to describe Native peoples of the North.

If Jupiter is in the sky, take a look to get a size comparison. The Eskimo Nebula appears about the same size as Jupiter through a telescope. When you first see the nebula, it may appear as a double star. And it should be no surprise that it was discovered by the eighteenth-century astronomer William Herschel, famous for, among other things, his surveys of double stars.

To find the Eskimo Nebula, form a line between the twin's beltlines, and follow it to a point below Pollux's outer arm.

Date/Time: _____

Location: _____

Weather/Seeing: _____

Notes: _____

_____

Moon Phase:	Sketch:
⊙ ____	

WINTER

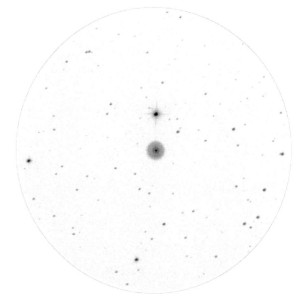

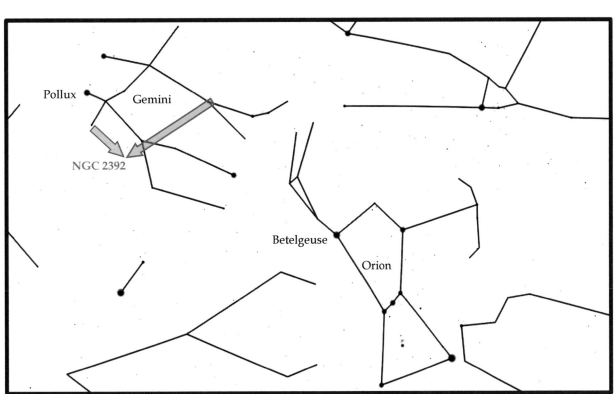

6. M35 & NGC 2158

M35 is an open cluster about the size of the full Moon (an open cluster is a group of stars loosely bound by gravity). Its brightness makes it a wonderful target for urban stargazing.

This cluster is so bright that it can be seen without a telescope in dark skies, or with binoculars in urban skies. Right next to it is another open cluster, NGC 2158 (NCG stands for "New General Catalog"). This second cluster is dimmer and denser.

Using an eyepiece with low magnification, you should be able to fit both these clusters into your field of view. Don't forget to record your observation and sketch what you see in the chart to the right.

To find M35, follow a line passing through the leftmost star in Orion's belt, and up through the bright orange star Betelgeuse. Then, identify the stars in the Gemini Twins' feet, and follow them to the right.

| Date/Time: _____ |
| Location: _____ |
| Weather/Seeing: _____ |
| Notes: _____ |

Moon Phase:	Sketch:

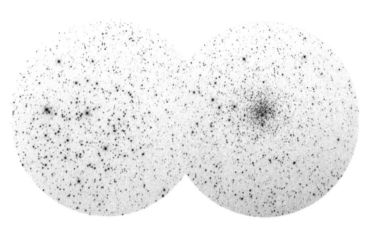

M35 (Left) and NGC 2158 (Right)

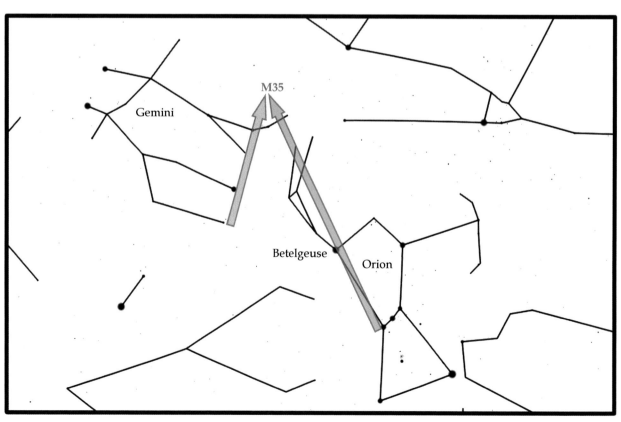

7. Satellite Cluster (NGC 2244)

The Satellite Cluster is an open star cluster, located to the left of the Orion constellation in the constellation Monoceros.

This cluster is a prime target for astrophotographers. This is because the Satellite Cluster, when photographed, becomes the Rosette Nebula, a sea of swirling red gas, dust, and plasma.

As you can see in the "telescope view" on the right, you can barely see any of the cloudy nebula belonging to the Rosette. This is because I used a short exposure to simulate the view through a telescope (a longer camera exposure would have revealed detail in the background nebula invisible to the human eye).

To find the Satellite Cluster, extend a line from Orion's shoulders. The cluster resides near the relatively bright star Epsilon Monocerotis.

Date/Time: _____

Location: _____

Weather/Seeing: _____

Notes: _____

_____

Moon Phase: ———

Sketch:

WINTER

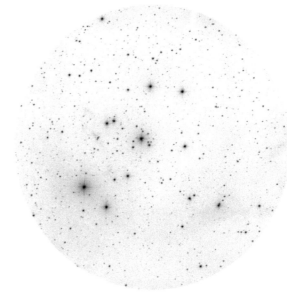

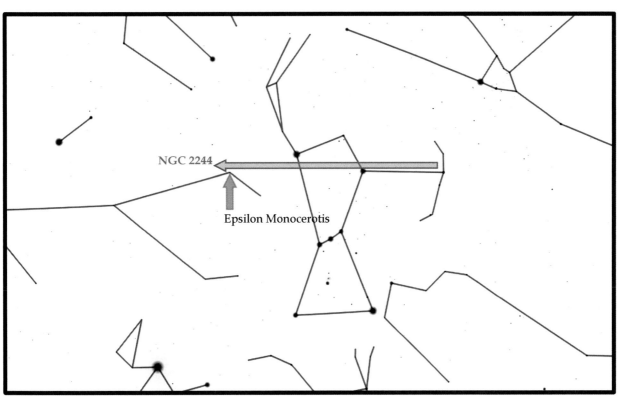

8. Caldwell 7 (NGC 2403)

In *50 Things to See with a Small Telescope*, we explored my two favorite galaxies, M81 (Bode's) and M82 (the Cigar). While these two galaxies should be revisited during almost any observing session, they have a lesser known neighbor, one that didn't make Charles Messier's "M" list of "things that aren't comets."

Caldwell 7 is a galaxy eight million light-years distant, and is a part of the M81 group of galaxies. This simply means that these galaxies interact gravitationally, or in scientific terms, the galaxies are *gravitationally bound.*

We'll find Caldwell 7 almost the same way we found M81 and M82 (creating a line between two stars in the asterism, The Big Dipper). Except this time, we'll need to add a reference star from the full constellation Ursa Major. Extend a line of equal length from the reference stars as shown below. Don't forget to be patient in your search. With a lack of nearby reference stars, finding Caldwell 7 can be a challenge.

Date/Time: _____

Location: _____

Weather/Seeing: _____

Notes: _____

_____

Moon Phase:

Sketch:

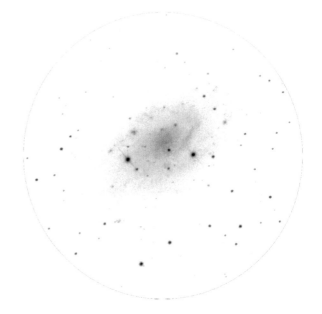

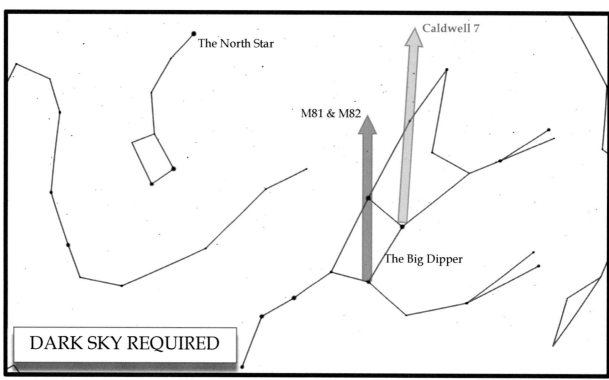

The North Star

Caldwell 7

M81 & M82

The Big Dipper

DARK SKY REQUIRED

9. Heart-Shaped Cluster (M50)

The Heart-Shaped Cluster resides in the relatively dim constellation Monoceros. Charles Messier first chronicled this cluster while taking note of a nearby comet, in 1772.

The cluster was given its common name by stargazers John Mallas and Evered Kreimer, when they described it as "Heart-Shaped" in their book, *The Messier Album*.

What shape do you see when you observe this cluster?

To find the Heart-Shaped Cluster, use Orion's belt as a reference, and then identify the bright star Sirius in the constellation Canis Major (which means "Greater Dog" in Latin). Identify the nose of the "dog," and follow a line from Sirius through the dog's nose to find the cluster.

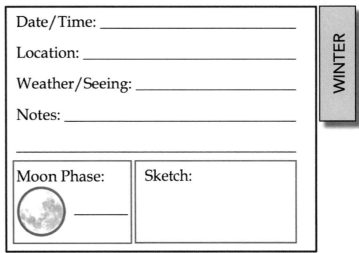

Date/Time: _____

Location: _____

Weather/Seeing: _____

Notes: _____

_____

Moon Phase: _____   Sketch:

WINTER

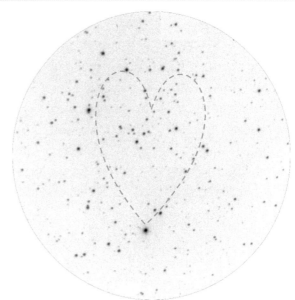

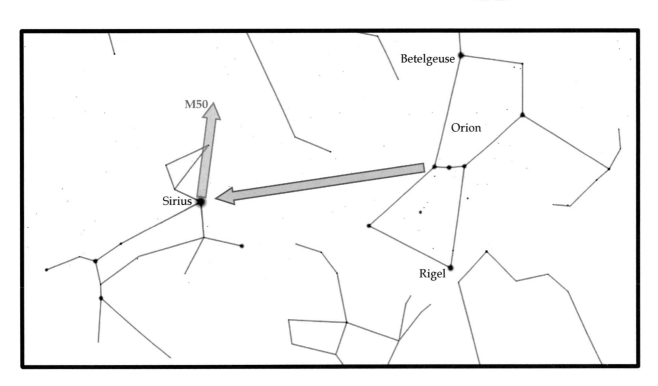

10. The Other Double Cluster (M46 and M47)

In my first book, *50 Things to See with a Small Telescope*, we explored a double cluster found near the constellation Cassiopeia. This book will explore another double cluster. M46 and M47 are technically within the constellation Puppis, though they are more easily found relative to Canis Major. (Puppis means "Poop Deck" in Latin… if you were wondering).

These clusters are close enough to pan between when using a low magnification. If your eyepiece field of view is wide enough, you may be able to see both targets in the same frame. M46 is the dimmest of the pair, and will require dark skies for optimal views. This cluster also contains a rare treat: planetary nebula NGC 2438 will appear in VERY dark skies.

To find M46 and M47, use Orion to find Sirius, then Mirzam. Then, trace a line through Mirzam and Sirius to find M47. M46 is right next to it.

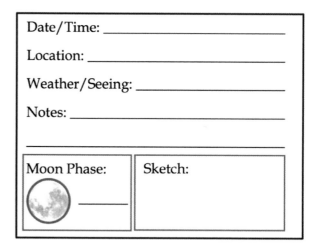

Date/Time: _____

Location: _____

Weather/Seeing: _____

Notes: _____

_____

Moon Phase: _____

Sketch:

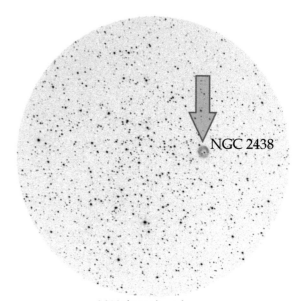

M46 through a telescope

NGC 2438

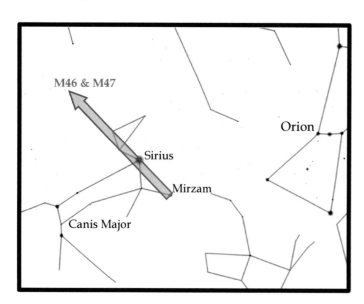

M46 & M47

Orion

Sirius

Mirzam

Canis Major

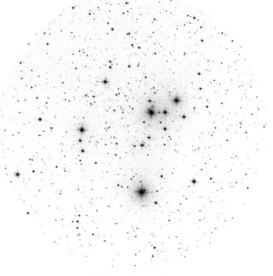

M47 through a telescope

11. The Cloaking Warbird (M37)

This magnificent star cluster, in the constellation Auriga, contains over five hundred stars. It is the perfect target for the mid-sized telescope, since it takes a larger aperture to resolve this cluster into individual stars. In smaller telescopes, it almost looks like a nebula.

While researching for this book, I could not find a common name for M37 (correct me if I'm wrong, and I'll update the book), so I'll put forward my own: The Cloaking Warbird, for the cluster's central structure's resemblance to a cloaking Romulan starship (from *Star Trek*)!

The whole cluster is relatively large, and, at high magnification, may exceed your field of view. I **love** it when this happens. The ability to pan around an astronomical object gives me the feeling of a true explorer.

To find M37, use Orion to hop over to the bright star Aldebaran. Use this star to find the two reference stars in Auriga. M37 is found between, and slightly below, these two stars.

| Date/Time: _____ |
| Location: _____ |
| Weather/Seeing: _____ |
| Notes: _____ |
| _____ |

WINTER

Moon Phase: _____

Sketch:

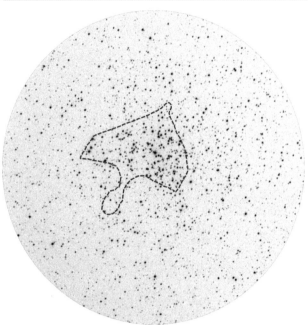

Dashed outline added by author

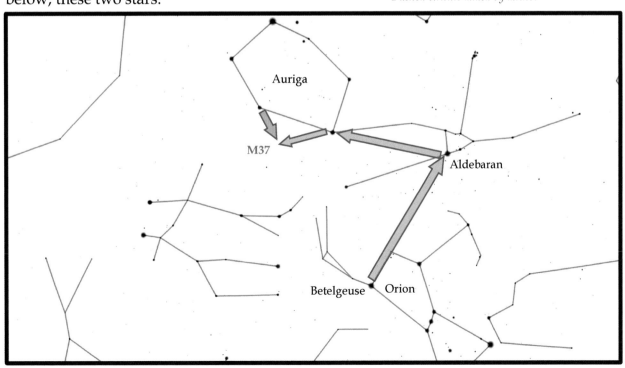

12. The "37" Cluster (NGC 2169)

The "37" Cluster is a grouping of stars that appear to form, you guessed it, the number 37. However, some telescopes invert or flip the image, so it's possible that it looks something like this through your telescope: **37**

The "37" can also be classified as two clusters. The first, making up the "3," is called Collinder 38. The "7" is named Collinder 83.

Amateur astronomers frequently refer to an object's magnitude when describing its brightness. To simplify this book, I've left any mention of magnitude out. However, you can do a little test. In the darkest skies, the human eye can see objects as dim as the sixth magnitude (the higher the number, the dimmer the object). This cluster lies just beyond what the human eye can perceive. Without magnification, while pointed at the "37" Cluster, it will appear that your telescope is fixed at a starless point in the sky!

Cluster "37" lies along Orion's right arm, above the bright orange star Betelgeuse.

Date/Time: _____	
Location: _____	
Weather/Seeing: _____	
Notes: _____	
_____	
Moon Phase: _____	Sketch:

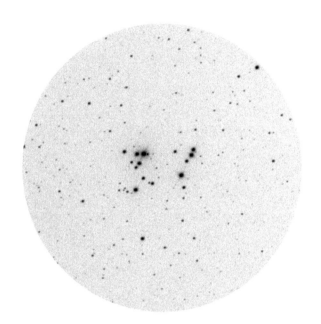

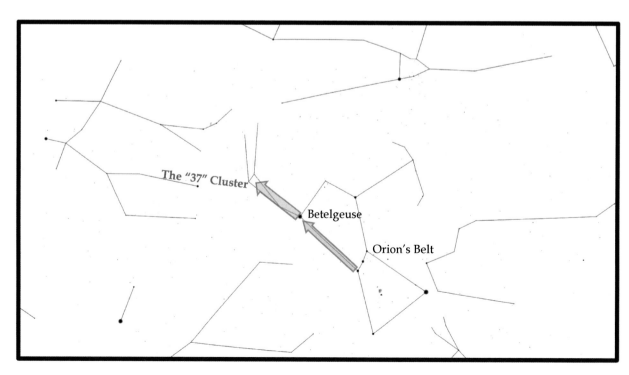

13. Starfish Cluster (M38)

After admiring M37, hop over to the center of the constellation Auriga to find the Starfish Cluster. This cluster contains very defined star patterns that some folks describe as the Greek letter pi, which looks like this: π

This cluster is filled with bluish stars, peppered with a few red giants.

The constellation Auriga is a polygon shape filled with several open star clusters, including the following: M36, NGC 1857, NGC 1778, NGC 1907, and NGC 1893. Pan your telescope in an expanding circle around M38 to explore each of these additional targets!

To find M38, identify the top and bottom stars in Auriga. This will get you oriented. The top star is Capella, (which you should also check out; it is a beautiful multi-star system) and the bottom star is Alnath. Once you are oriented, M38 is located directly between the two side stars, as shown in the map below.

Date/Time: _____

Location: _____

Weather/Seeing: _____

Notes: _____

_____

Moon Phase: _____

Sketch:

WINTER

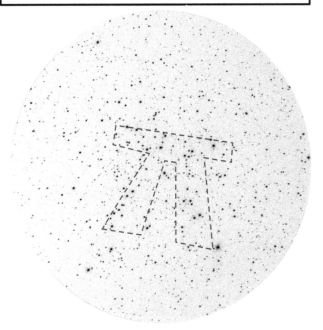

Dashed lines added by author

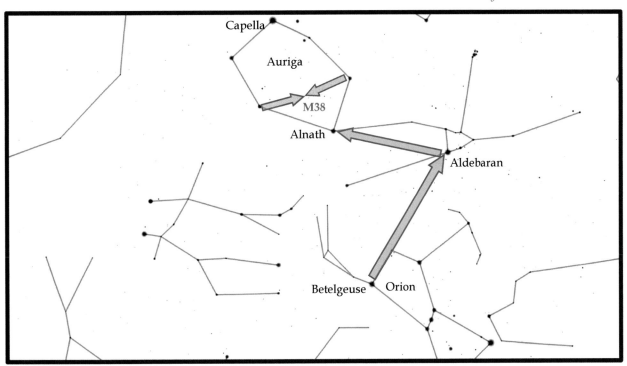

27

SPRING

Say goodbye to Orion, as it drops below the western horizon. Leo is still high overhead, and if you have dark skies, it's a great place to hunt for galaxies. Hercules, with its great globular cluster (M13), begins rising from the east. Soon, M13 will be added to your nightly stargazing repertoire. You'll know warmer weather is on its way when the summer triangle (Deneb, Altair, and Vega) climbs into the evening sky.

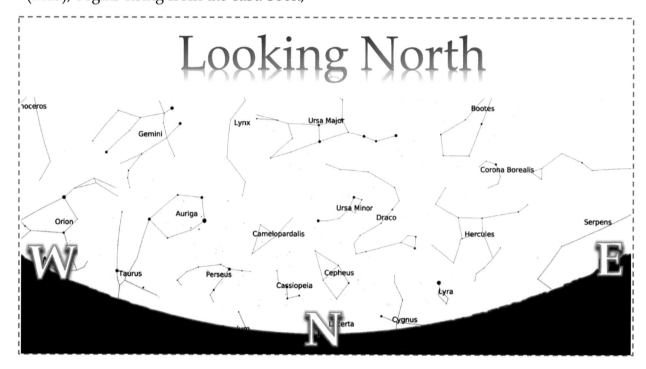

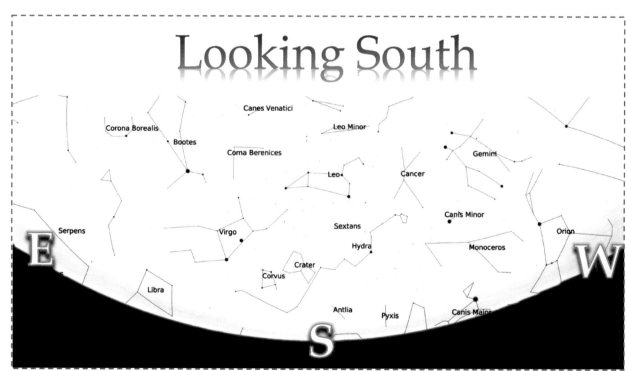

14. Beehive Star Cluster (M44)

The Beehive is visible to the naked eye on very clear nights in dark skies, and makes a great target for binoculars. However, in my experience, this object is obscure enough that often even seasoned stargazers have trouble locating it in the dim constellation Cancer. That's why I'm including it here.

This cluster has been known of since antiquity. The Greek mathematician and astronomer Claudius Ptolemy, who lived in the second century, noted the cluster to be a nebulous mass (cloudy-like). Telescopic observations revealed that this was merely the result of the close grouping of stars within the cluster.

The cluster is quite large, measuring more than three times the diameter of the full Moon. When observing, use an eyepiece with minimal magnification and a wide field of view.

The Beehive Cluster lies between the bright stars Regulus (in Leo) and Pollux (in Gemini), and between two dimmer center stars in Cancer.

Date/Time: _____

Location: _____

Weather/Seeing: _____

Notes: _____
_____

Moon Phase: _____

Sketch:

SPRING

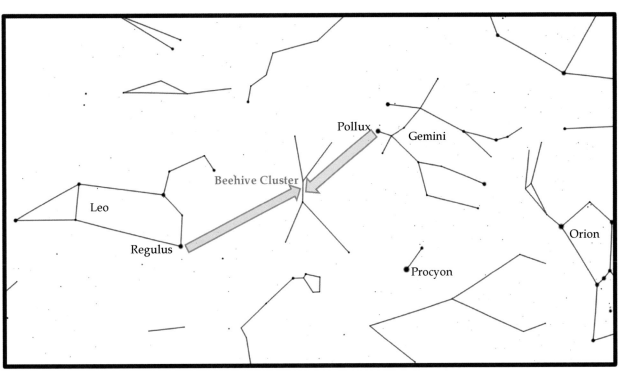

15. Algieba

Algieba (also known as Gamma Leonis) is a fantastic double star cataloged by William Herschel. This is a fine target for the spring, when Leo is high in the sky.

It can be a challenge, however, to split the two stars apart in your field of view. You'll need high magnification, and steady skies. But, when you finally "split the double," you'll be rewarded with this double star's unique blend of brilliant yellow from one star and bright orange from the other.

In 2009, a team of astronomers discovered a large object orbiting the larger star of the pair. The object has an estimated mass of eight times that of Jupiter. Professional astronomers refer to it as "sub-stellar", since the object is not quite large enough to be a star, but is almost too big to be called a planet. More research is needed to refine the object's classification[1].

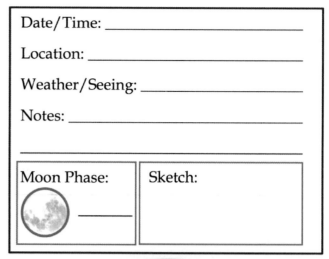

Date/Time: _____

Location: _____

Weather/Seeing: _____

Notes: _____

_____

Moon Phase: _____

Sketch:

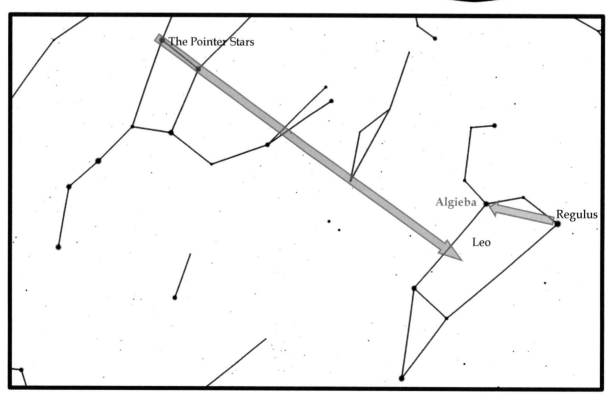

The Pointer Stars

Algieba

Regulus

Leo

[1]Astronomy and Astrophysics: http://www.aanda.org/articles/aa/abs/2010/01/aa12536-09/aa12536-09.html

16. Leo Triplet

The Leo Triplet consists of three galaxies that almost fit into a single wide-field eyepiece field of view. These objects are quite dim compared to most of the items listed in this book, and they are difficult to observe under urban skies. If the sky appears rich with stars without a telescope (like the image below), these galaxies should be visible through one.

Date/Time: _____

Location: _____

Weather/Seeing: _____

Notes: _____

SPRING

NGC 3628
(Hamburger Galaxy)

M66 is the brightest object in the group. The other two galaxies are named M65 and NGC 3628 (nicknamed the Hamburger Galaxy).

Though Leo is supposed to be a lion, I often picture him as a mouse, with the triangle on his left representing the head. To find the Leo Triplet, look just below the mouse's neck.

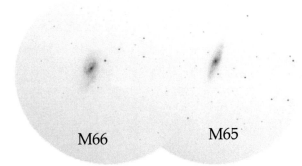

M66   M65

MOONLESS NIGHT AND
DARK SKY REQUIRED

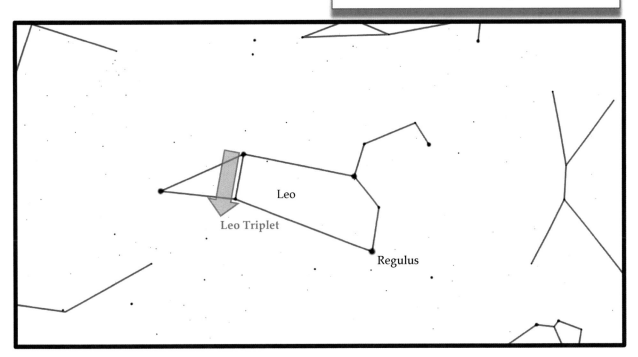

17. M96 Galaxy Trio

Leo contains a second trio of galaxies, called the M96 Cluster. These galaxies are designated M96, M95, and M105. M105 is the dimmest of these galaxies, and may be the most difficult to see. However, M95 and M96 should be visible within a single frame using a wide-field eyepiece on moonless nights, at a fair distance from city lights.

I had little luck viewing these galaxies in even mildly light-polluted skies. When I was finally successful, I found M105 nearly impossible to resolve. Maybe you'll have better luck! In really dark skies you may be able to resolve two companion galaxies to M105. These are named NGC 3384 and 3389.

To find the Galaxy Trio, scan the area below the constellation Leo, as shown below. To find the dark-sky location nearest you, visit:

http://darksitefinder.com

MOONLESS NIGHT AND DARK SKY REQUIRED

Date/Time: _____

Location: _____

Weather/Seeing: _____

Notes: _____

Moon Phase: _____

Sketch:

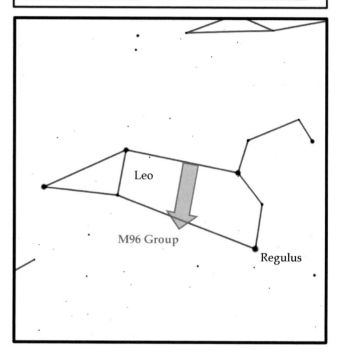

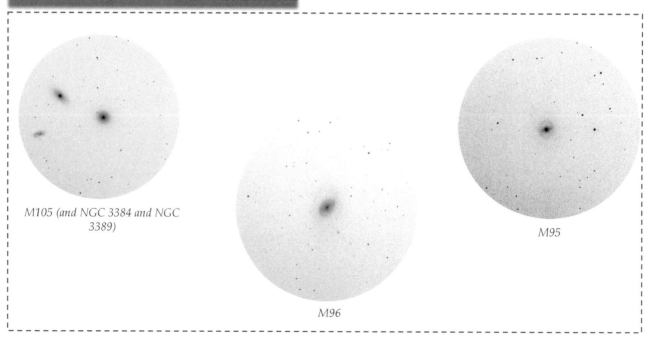

M105 (and NGC 3384 and NGC 3389)

M96

M95

18. Messier 3

M3 is one of the biggest and brightest globular clusters in the sky, and is only slightly less intense than M13 in Hercules (mentioned in *50 Things to See with a Small Telescope*).

This cluster contains an estimated half a million stars, and is located about thirty-four thousand light-years from Earth. This is farther than the center of the Milky Way Galaxy, which is only about twenty-six thousand light-years from our Solar System.

One distinguishing quality of M3 is that the cluster appears as if enclosed in a triangle of three bright stars.

To find M3, use the big dipper to "Arc to Arcturus," and then form a triangle using the reference stars in the constellation Bootes to narrow in on this Globular Custer.

Date/Time: _____

Location: _____

Weather/Seeing: _____

Notes: _____

_____

Moon Phase: _____

Sketch:

SPRING

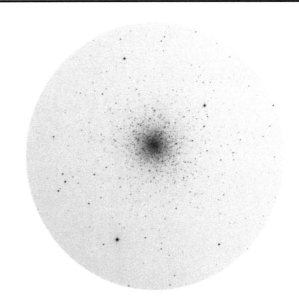

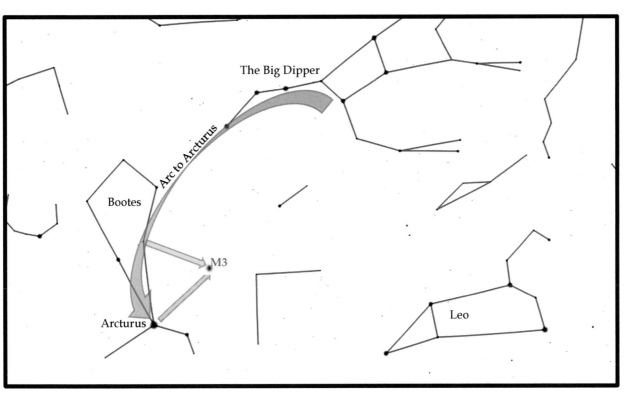

19. Sunflower Galaxy (M63)

The spring is definitely galaxy season, and spiral galaxy M63 is an easy target to add to your observing list. Though located thirty-seven million light-years from Earth, the galaxy is relatively bright and is easy to find in most mid-sized scopes. However, you may need an eight-inch scope, and dark skies, before you see any detail from the spiral arms.

This galaxy is in the same group as the Whirlpool Galaxy, M51 (mentioned in the book *50 Things to See with a Small Telescope*). By "group," astronomers mean that these galaxies interact gravitationally.

To find M63, use the star at the end of the handle in the Big Dipper and the star Cor Caroli as references. M63 lies between these two stars, at a distance equal to the space between two stars in the handle of the Big Dipper.

Date/Time: _____

Location: _____

Weather/Seeing: _____

Notes: _____

_____

Moon Phase: _____

Sketch:

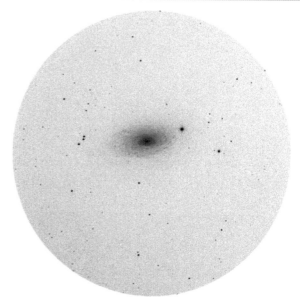

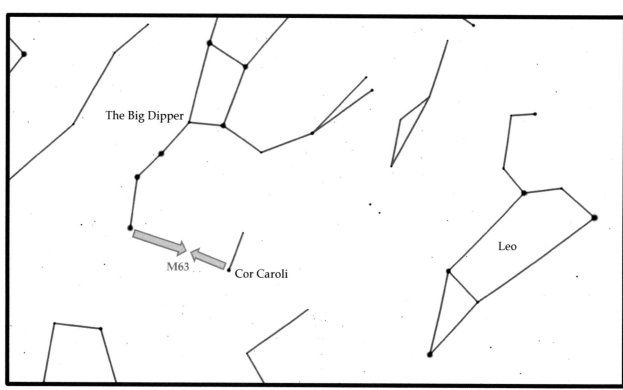

The Big Dipper

M63

Cor Caroli

Leo

20. Pinwheel Galaxy (M101)

M101 is a wonderful spiral galaxy in the Big Dipper. Due to its position in the northern sky, it makes a great dark-sky target most nights of the year.

I did most of my early observing near San Francisco, and despite several attempts using a twelve-inch Dobsonian telescope, I was unable to see M101 through light-polluted skies.

Then, during a star party at Glacier Point in Yosemite National Park, this beauty came into view in a mid-sized Newtonian telescope I'd borrowed for the trip! The borrowed scope, which was only a quarter as powerful as my Dobsonian, rewarded me with superior views thanks to Yosemite's clear, dark skies. The galaxy's spiral arms were superbly defined, and occupied much of my telescope's field of view.

To find M101, form a triangle with the two farthest stars in the handle of the Big Dipper.

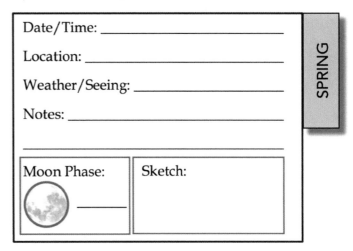

Date/Time: _____

Location: _____

Weather/Seeing: _____

Notes: _____

_____

Moon Phase: _____   Sketch:

SPRING

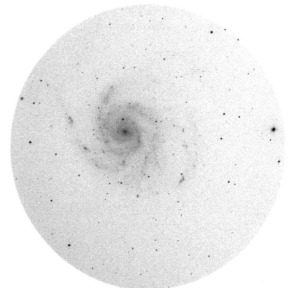

How M101 appeared at Glacier Point

MOONLESS NIGHT AND
DARK SKY REQUIRED

The Big Dipper

The North Star

M101

Arcturus

21. Cat's Eye Galaxy (M94)

M94 is a spiral galaxy in the small constellation Canes Venatici, located below the Big Dipper. Lately, this galaxy has been of particular interest to astronomers studying Dark Matter, as it appears to have a shortage of these mysterious particles[1].

While researching for this book, I was unable to determine who first coined the phrase "Cat's Eye" or "Croc's Eye." The early descriptions by Charles Messier and William Herschel do not include a nickname. However, the "eye" seems to be derived from the galaxy's classification as a bar galaxy, although this galaxy's actual central bar structure is less defined than most.

To find M94, follow the tip of the Big Dipper's handle down to a bright double star called Cor Caroli, and then look back up toward the dipper.

| Date/Time: _____ |
| Location: _____ |
| Weather/Seeing: _____ |
| Notes: _____ |

Moon Phase: _____   Sketch:

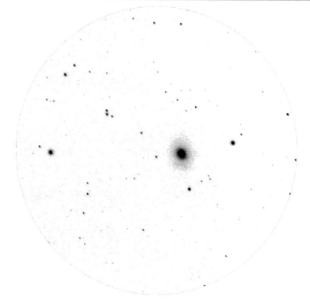

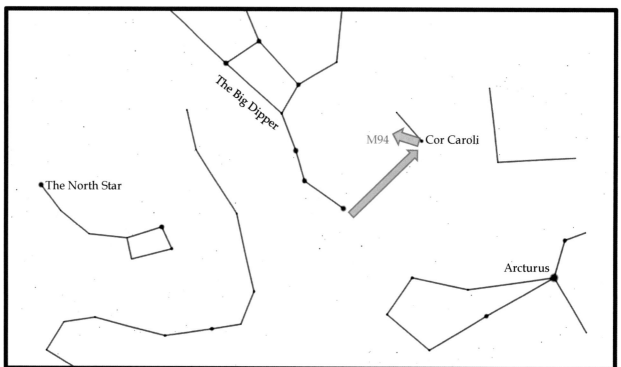

[1] Cornell University Library: http://arxiv.org/abs/astro-ph/0611113

22. Sombrero Galaxy (M104)

Late in the spring, this southern galaxy rises to its highest point in the sky. M104, the Sombrero Galaxy, is one of the brightest Messier Galaxies, but for me, it was a very challenging one to find.

Interestingly, M104 wasn't included in Charles Messier's original catalog (his final catalog included in the French astronomical publication *Connoissance des Temps* ended with his 103rd object). Messier observed M104 in 1781, noting its location. Because of this note, it was finally added to the list of "M" objects in 1921.

To locate the Sombrero Galaxy, first find Virgo and Spica by following the phrase "Arc to Arcturus, Speed to Spica." Then form a triangle between Spica and neighboring star Porrima to find the M104.

Date/Time: _____

Location: _____

Weather/Seeing: _____

Notes: _____

_____

Moon Phase: _____   Sketch:

SPRING

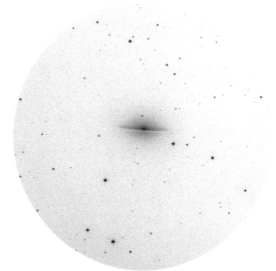

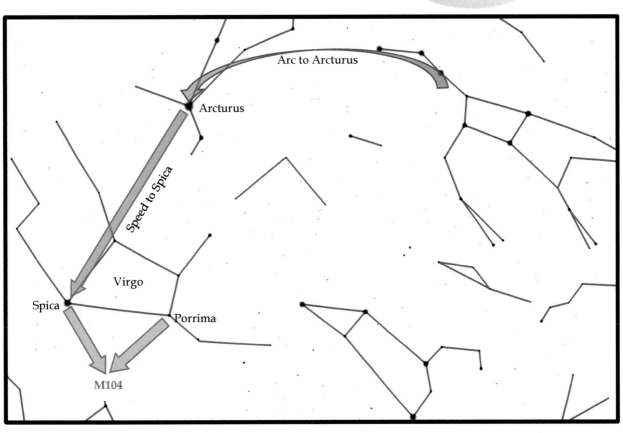

23. M53

M53 is a great globular cluster for this season, and will also be used as a reference for finding M64, detailed in the next section.

M53 is located in the constellation Coma Berenices, a constellation difficult to identify in suburban skies. However, this constellation contains a surprisingly large number of deep-sky targets, including Messier's objects: M53, M64, M85, M88, M91, M98, M99, and M100.

To find M53, first identify the star Diadem, which is almost directly between Arcturus and Denebola, the star in the lion's tail (or, as I see it, the mouse's nose). Once you have Diadem centered in your field of view, you should be able to see M53 off to the side.

Date/Time: _____

Location: _____

Weather/Seeing: _____

Notes: _____

_____

Moon Phase: _____

Sketch:

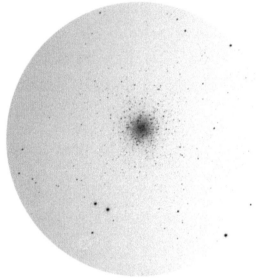

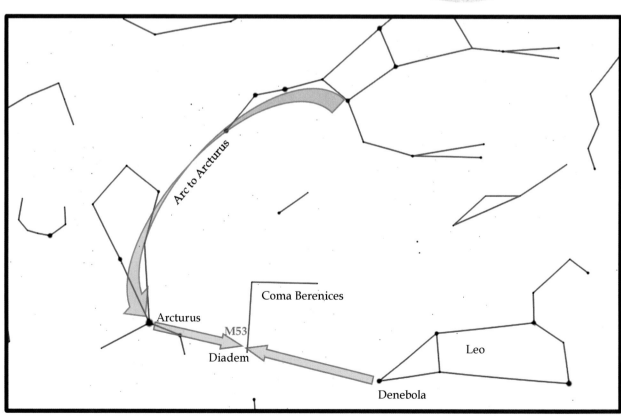

24. Black Eye Galaxy (M64)

The name "Black Eye Galaxy" was coined by none other than British astronomer Sir William Herschel, the man who discovered Uranus. In looking at this image from the Hubble Space Telescope, you can clearly see why some even call M64 the "Evil Eye."

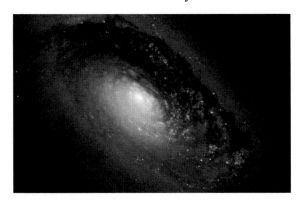

M64 imaged by the Hubble Space Telescope

M64 is found halfway between Arcturus (remember to "Arc to Arcturus") and Leo. It is located in Coma Berenices, near the star Diadem. If you found M53 in the previous section, simply find it again, and point your telescope up, just a bit, to narrow in on M64.

Date/Time: _____

Location: _____

Weather/Seeing: _____

Notes: _____

_____

Moon Phase: _____   Sketch:

SPRING

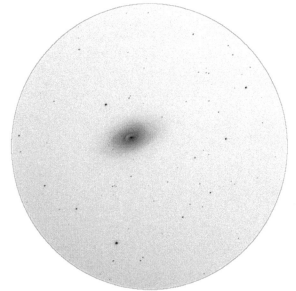

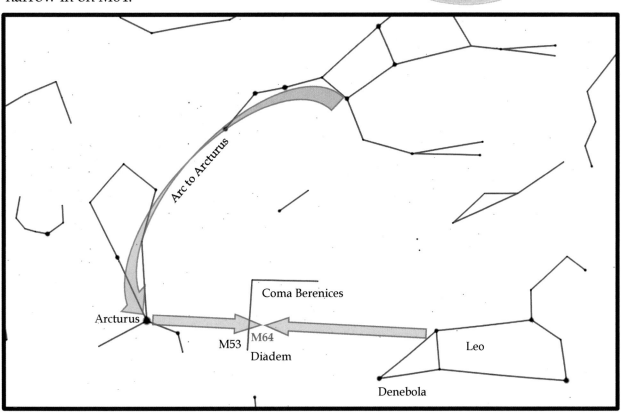

Arc to Arcturus

Coma Berenices

Arcturus

M53 | M64

Diadem

Leo

Denebola

25. Izar (Epsilon Boötis)

This double star is definitely a challenge for smaller telescopes. It requires at least four inches of aperture, and steady skies (although some folks claim to be able to separate both stars with less).

Once you do separate the double, which will take quite high magnification (a small diameter eyepiece), this delightful combination will reveal a yellow primary star with a blue-white companion.

Some double stars are too bright for the sensors on many CCD cameras, with both stars appearing as one. For this reason, the "telescope view" image for Izar (and Algieba too) has been simulated using astronomy software.

To find Izar, **don't** "Arc to Arcturus." Instead, jump straight across the sky using the two outer stars in the handle of the Big Dipper.

Date/Time: _____

Location: _____

Weather/Seeing: _____

Notes: _____

_____

Moon Phase: _____

Sketch:

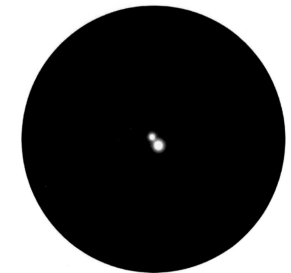

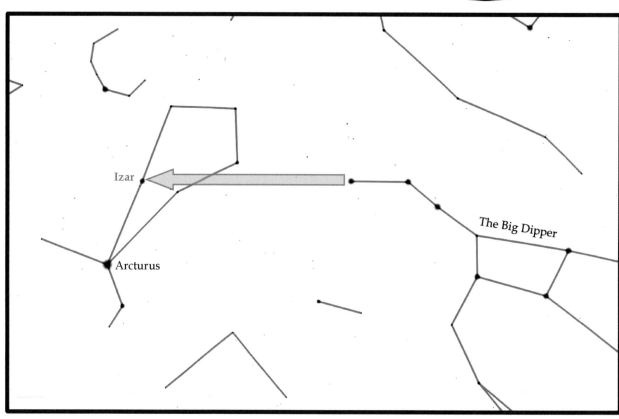

Izar

Arcturus

The Big Dipper

26. Winnecke 4 (M40)

Winnecke 4 is, effectively, the nebula that never was. When this object was added to Charles Messier's catalog, he was attempting to find a nebula reported by another astronomer named Johann Hevelius[1]. Messier never found Hevelius' nebula. Instead he recorded the location of this double star.

However, Winnecke 4 is not even a binary star. It's a visual double, two stars that appear close together but are not actually bound by gravity. Their only connection to one another is a coincidental line of sight.

To find this visual double, use the star Megrez (where the handle meets the cup of the Big Dipper), and move upward to a yellow star named 70 UMa. M40 will be the double star right above 70 UMa.

Date/Time: _____

Location: _____

Weather/Seeing: _____

Notes: _____

_____

Moon Phase: ⃝ _____

Sketch:

SPRING

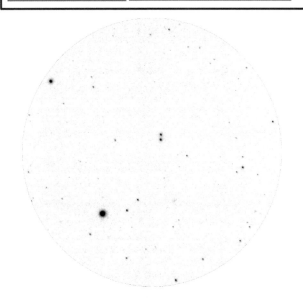

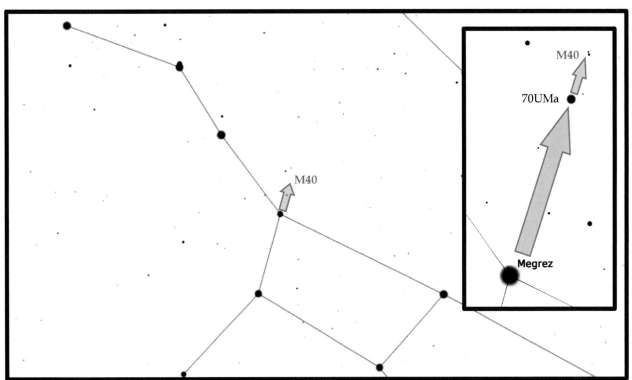

[1]Students for the Exploration and Development of Space (SEDS): http://messier.seds.org/m/m040.html

SUMMER

With BBQ and camping season off to a wonderful beginning, every youthful soul dreams of spending at least one night under the stars. There's something magical about a warm summer's evening, searching for shooting stars and talking about life. The avid stargazer begins his night with a quick look at M13, the great globular cluster in Hercules, swings by Lyra to admire the ring nebula, checks out galaxy pair M81 and M82, and then turns to appreciate any planets that just happen to be hanging around.

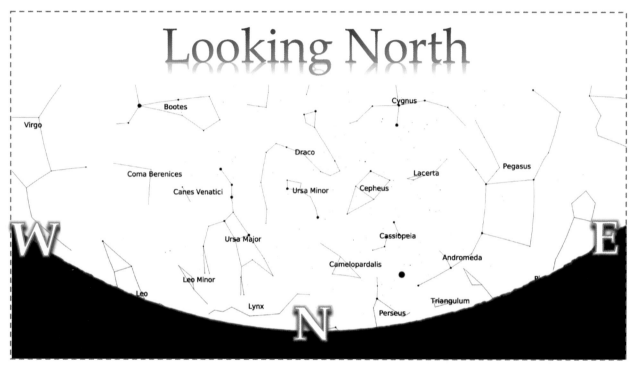

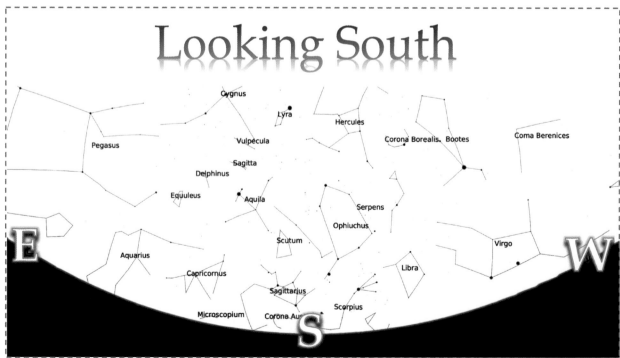

27. M5

Globular cluster M5 is one of the brightest deep-sky objects. However, its location in the sky, far from bright reference stars, makes it a challenge to find. For optimal viewing, look for this cluster high in the southern sky during late spring and early summer.

Several notable astronomers came upon M5 while searching for comets. Both Charles Messier and Johann Elert Bode recorded this cluster in their logs, noting it as "a nebula without stars." Isn't it wondrous that today's mid-sized telescopes can distinguish more detail than those used by comet hunters in the 1700s?

You'll find M5 about halfway between Arcturus and Graffias. For extra help, use the star Spica to identify additional reference stars in Virgo.

Date/Time: _____

Location: _____

Weather/Seeing: _____

Notes: _____

_____

Moon Phase: _____

Sketch:

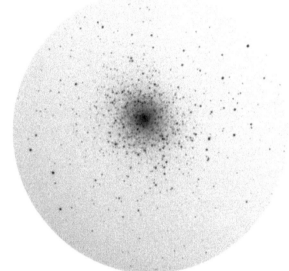

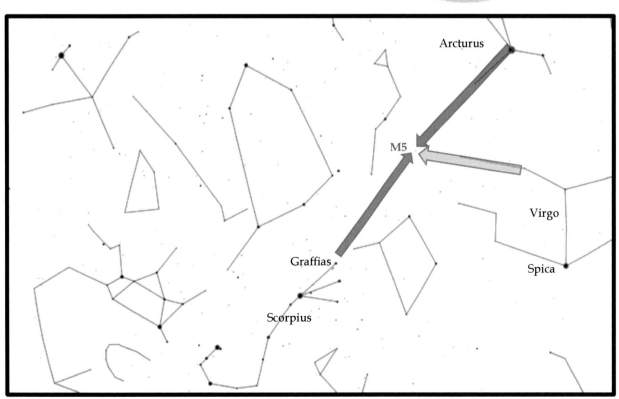

28. Omega Nebula (M17)

In *50 Things to See with a Small Telescope*, we introduced the cornucopia of deep-sky beauties in Sagittarius. With a mid-sized telescope, there's even more to explore!

"The Teapot" is a name for the star pattern within the constellation Sagittarius. As you can see in the map below, lining up the stars will lead you to several fantastic targets.

Just like the Great Nebula in Orion, the Omega Nebula is what astronomers call a "star factory," where dust and gas swirl together under gravity's influence to form new stars.

The primary target here is the Omega Nebula (M17), but several other targets are close by:

- Globular Clusters M22 and M28
- Sagittarius Star Cloud M24
- Open Cluster M25

Date/Time: _____

Location: _____

Weather/Seeing: _____

Notes: _____

_____

Moon Phase: _____

Sketch:

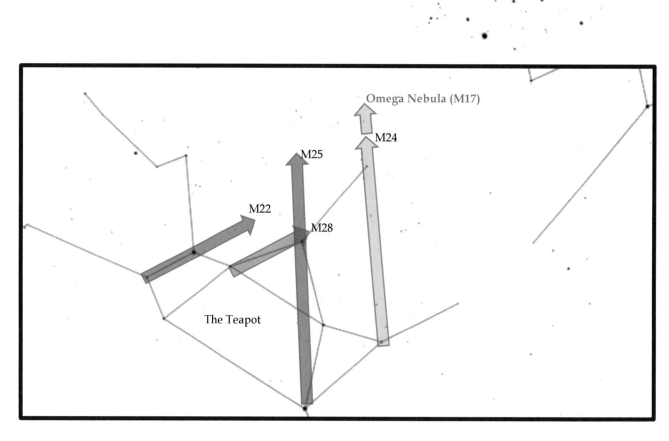

29. The Double-Double (Epsilon Lyrae)

In *50 Things to See with a Small Telescope*, we explored the stars named Mizar and Alcor, where Mizar can be further split into two stars through a telescope. This set of double stars is similar in that it's possible to distinguish a binary system with the naked eye. However, unlike Mizar and Alcor, both stars in Epsilon Lyrae can be divided once again.

Epsilon Lyrae is quite easy to find, as it sits right beside Vega in the constellation Lyra at the top of the Summer Triangle.

Epsilon Lyrae is beautiful as a double star, alone. When I first observed it with an eight-inch telescope, I could not make out the true "double-double." It wasn't until I added a 2x Barlow, doubling the magnification, that the Double-Double came into clear view.

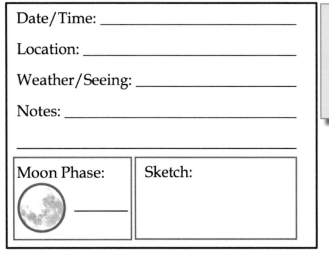

Date/Time: _____

Location: _____

Weather/Seeing: _____

Notes: _____

_____

Moon Phase: _____   Sketch:

SUMMER

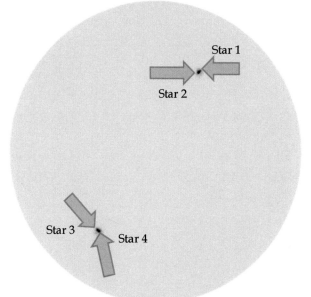

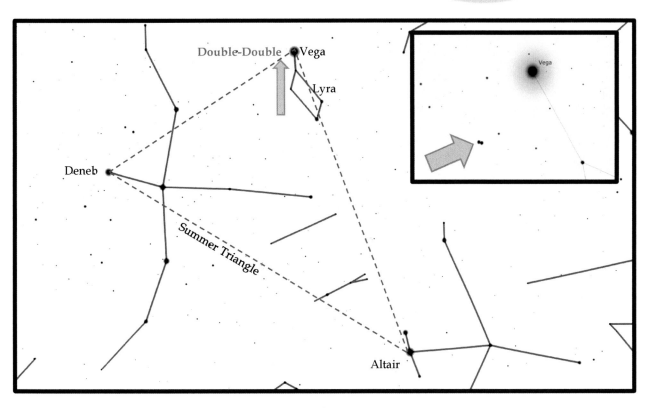

30. The Coathanger

When I started writing this book, I wanted to find targets that were interesting and outside the norm, yet easy to find. The Coathanger, also known as Brocchi's Cluster, is my new favorite star party object.

The Coathanger is typically a binocular target, but a mid-sized telescope with a low-power (and wide field) eyepiece provides incredible views of these multicolored stars. Using a 35mm eyepiece in my eight-inch reflector, I was able to fit the entire cluster into my field of view.

The cluster is located on the Summer Triangle, between Vega and Altair. Look for six bright stars lined up in a row, with an additional four stars making up the hook in the hanger. Pictures really don't do it justice.

| Date/Time: _____ |
| Location: _____ |
| Weather/Seeing: _____ |
| Notes: _____ |
| _____ |

Moon Phase:	Sketch:

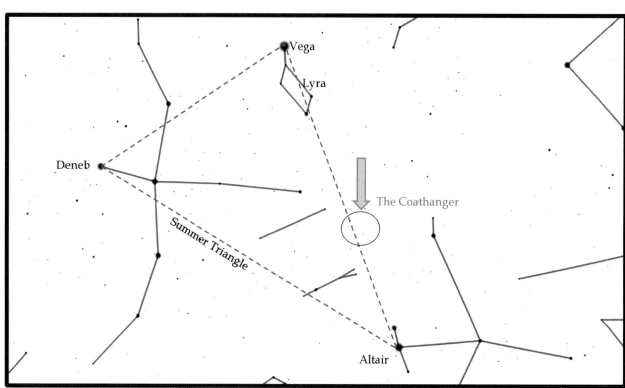

Vega

Lyra

Deneb

Summer Triangle

The Coathanger

Altair

31. Graffias (Acrab/Beta Scorpii)

The word "Graffias" means claws. This double star is located in the "Rake," which kind of looks like a claw. From Canada, where I'm sitting as I write this section of the book, Scorpius' tail is partially hidden by the horizon, but the Rake is clearly visible.

There is another nearby double star that some folks call Graffias. In fact, the Stellarium software calls this star Acrab, and the other star Graffias. However, the "Graffias" in the Rake has about three times the angular separation between the double stars, making it a much easier target!

Through some telescopes, the two observable stars in Graffias appear to be sitting on top of each other. Some astronomers refer to this configuration as "snowman style," where the smaller star almost appears stacked on top of the larger one.

Graffias is easy to find as the topmost star in Scorpius's "Rake".

Date/Time: _____

Location: _____

Weather/Seeing: _____

Notes: _____

_____

Moon Phase: _____

Sketch:

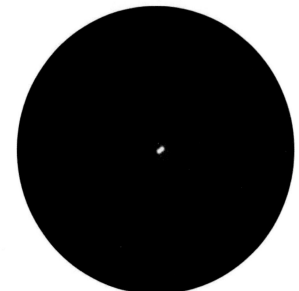

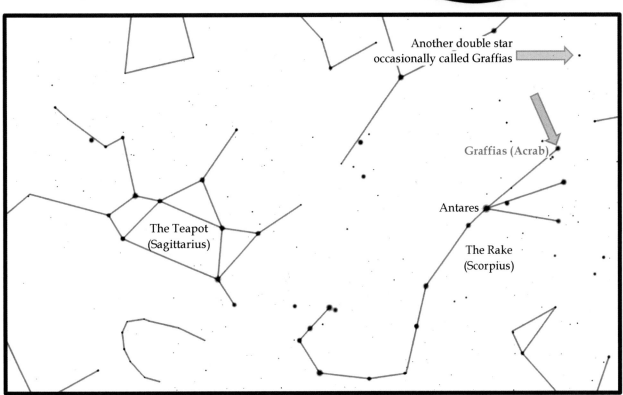

Another double star occasionally called Graffias

Graffias (Acrab)

Antares

The Teapot (Sagittarius)

The Rake (Scorpius)

32. M92

M92 is a globular star cluster in the constellation Hercules. I like to think of it as M13's next-door neighbor. When you're in the neighborhood of the great cluster in Hercules (M13), you might as well stop by M92 as well.

One bit of stellar trivia: due to the Earth's precession around its axis, in about fourteen thousand years, the Earth's celestial north pole will point near this cluster![1]

Start your search for M92 by identifying the "Keystone" (quadrilateral box) in the constellation Hercules. To determine on which side of the Keystone M92 lies, draw an imaginary line between Vega and the handle of the Big Dipper.

To find M92, form a triangle using the two Keystone stars parallel to the imaginary line above.

| Date/Time: _____ |
| Location: _____ |
| Weather/Seeing: _____ |
| Notes: _____ |
| _____ |

Moon Phase:	Sketch:

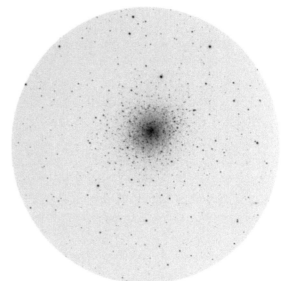

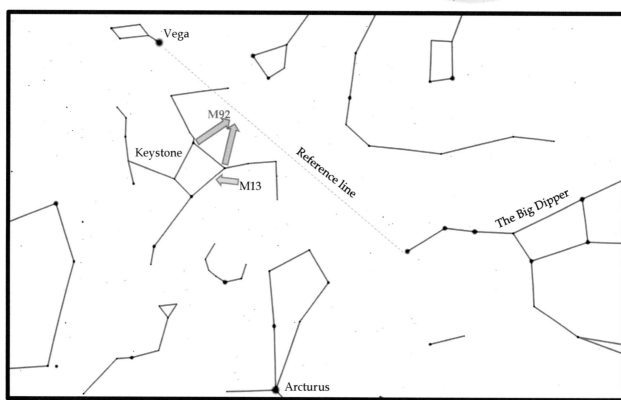

[1] Students for the Exploration and Development of Space (SEDS): http://messier.seds.org/m/m092.html

33. Butterfly Cluster (M6)

The Butterfly Cluster is an open cluster located approximately sixteen hundred light-years from Earth, and covers an area of sky about the size of the full Moon.

It's clear how the Butterfly Cluster got its name. With a bright orange star as the head, neighboring stars curve around the central spine to create wings, while nearby stars form the antenna.

You'll find the Butterfly Cluster between the star in the spout of the Teapot, and the central star in the constellation Scorpius.

It's fun to sketch the pattern. Below is the pattern traced over a photo I took at the 2016 Nova East Star Party.

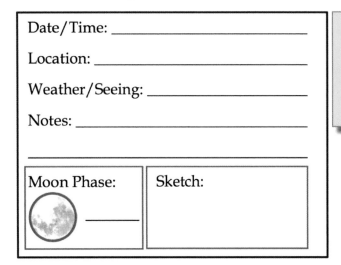

Date/Time: _____

Location: _____

Weather/Seeing: _____

Notes: _____

_____

Moon Phase: _____

Sketch:

SUMMER

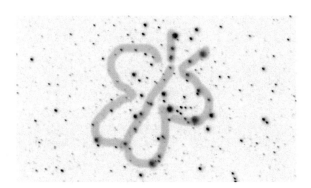

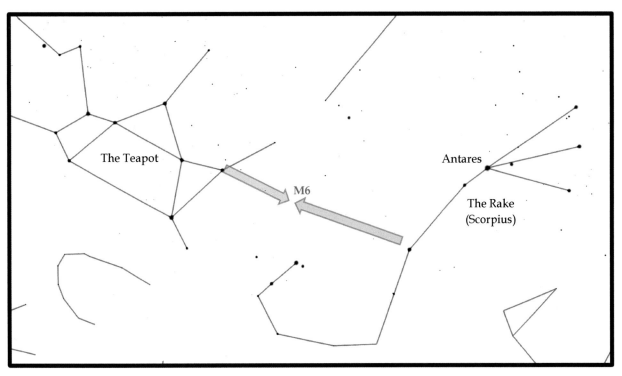

The Teapot

M6

Antares

The Rake
(Scorpius)

34. Eagle Nebula (M16)

You've definitely seen pictures of this nebula. It contains one of the Hubble Space Telescope's most famous images: *The Pillars of Creation* (below).

M16 is located about halfway between Altair (in the Summer Triangle) and Antares (in Scorpius). Use these reference points to identify the bottom two stars in the obscure constellation Scutum, and then follow an imaginary line up to M16.

| Date/Time: _____ |
| Location: _____ |
| Weather/Seeing: _____ |
| Notes: _____ |
| _____ |

Moon Phase: _____   Sketch:

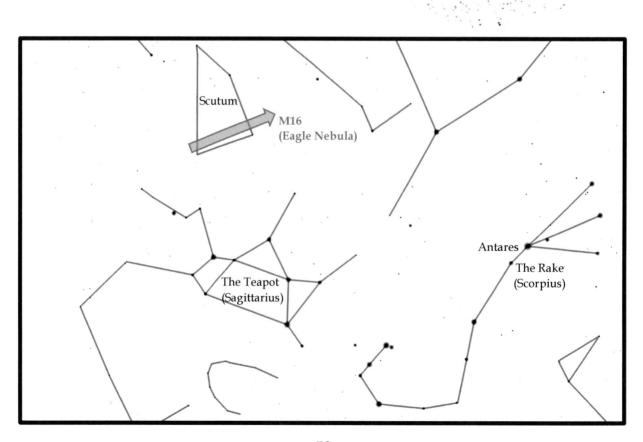

Scutum

M16 (Eagle Nebula)

Antares

The Rake (Scorpius)

The Teapot (Sagittarius)

35. Wild Duck Cluster (M11)

Though M11 is technically an open cluster (versus a globular cluster), the Wild Duck Cluster is tightly packed with stars, and gets its name for an apparent resemblance to a flock of ducks.

My good friend Paul Reid, the outreach lead at the Mount Diablo Astronomical Society (MDAS), calls this cluster "The Borg Cube," which I think is a far more fitting name.

What's the difference between open clusters and globular clusters? Open clusters tend to be made of young stars that spread out over time, whereas globular clusters contain thousands of very old stars.

To find M11, first identify the stars in the Summer Triangle. Then, locate the star at the tip of Aquila's tail (Aquila is Latin for eagle). Beginning with the tail star, curve up past two bordering stars to find M11.

Date/Time: _____

Location: _____

Weather/Seeing: _____

Notes: _____

_____

Moon Phase: _____ | Sketch:

SUMMER

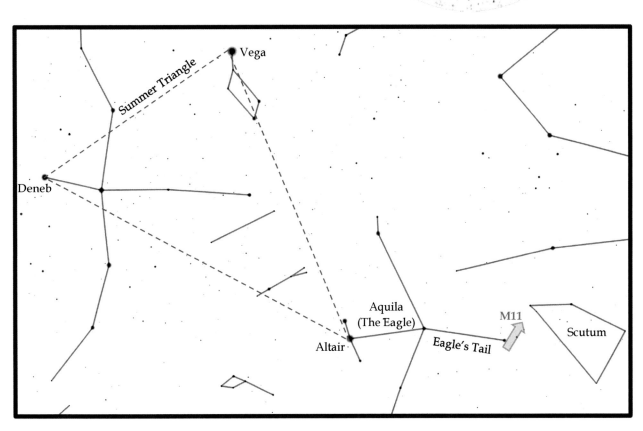

36. M56

For me, learning about the location of globular cluster M56 was a surprise. In 2013, I attended as many as four star parties per week, and not once did we look at M56, despite numerus viewing of the nearby Ring Nebula (one of my favorite targets from *50 Things to See with a Small Telescope*).

One of my favorite outreach activities is rapidly switching between similar objects (which you can easily learn to do with a non-computerized telescope and a Telrad, or other unit-power finders). Due to M56's convenient location between Lyra and Albireo, it makes a great candidate for comparing and contrasting with the popular stargazing target M13 (the Great Globular Cluster in Hercules).

M56 is located within the Summer Triangle, between the base of the Northern Cross (an asterism in the constellation Cygnus) and the base of the Diamond in Lyra.

Date/Time: _____

Location: _____

Weather/Seeing: _____

Notes: _____

_____

Moon Phase: _____

Sketch:

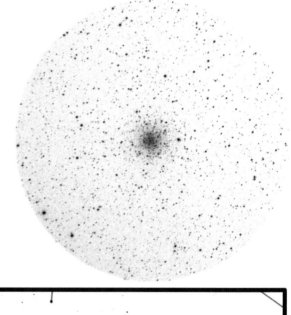

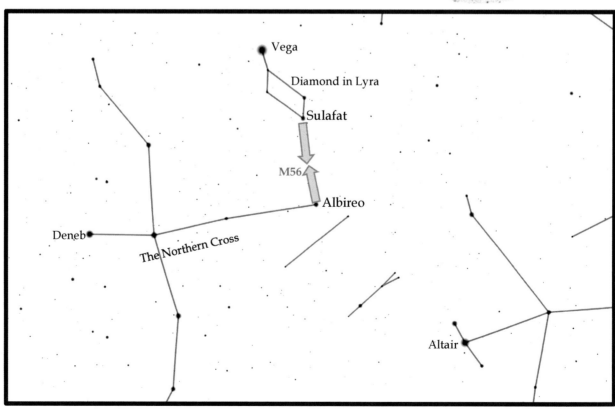

37. Hole in a Cluster (NGC 6811)

Hole in a Cluster is an open cluster deriving its name from stars distributed in an almost doughnut-like shape.

This cluster was of special interest to professional astronomers involved in NASA's Kepler mission, because it fell within the field of view of this space-telescope's exoplanet hunting camera. Kepler-66b and Kepler-67b were the first two planets that were discovered within this cluster[1].

The cluster isn't quite as large as the other open clusters listed in this book, so you won't need to use a wide-angle eyepiece to fit it all in. But don't go overboard on the magnification, either. Most deep-sky objects (targets outside of our Solar System) are best viewed at low to medium magnification.

This cluster is found just outside the Summer Triangle (Vega, Deneb, and Altair), past the right side of the Northern Cross.

Date/Time: _____

Location: _____

Weather/Seeing: _____

Notes: _____

_____

Moon Phase: _____   Sketch:

SUMMER

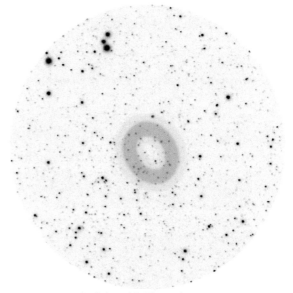

Color added by author

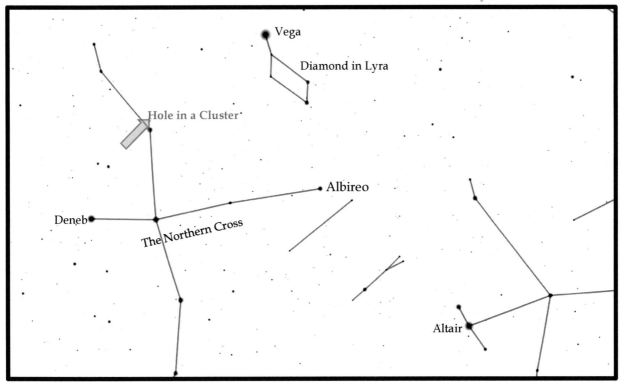

Vega

Diamond in Lyra

Hole in a Cluster

Albireo

Deneb

The Northern Cross

Altair

[1] Harvard-Smithsonian Center for Astrophysics: https://www.cfa.harvard.edu/news/2013-17

38. The Summer Beehive (IC 4665)

While typically a target for binoculars, a larger telescope reveals many more stars within this cluster. This cluster is designated IC 4665. The IC stands for "Index Catalog," a supplementary catalog to the NGC (New General Catalog).

What makes this a great star party target? When observing this cluster, many people see the word "HI" written in the star, as if aliens are sending us a "how do you do?"

This cluster is located in a part of the sky lacking in bright reference stars, but here's how I find it: follow a line emanating from the bottom of the Northern Cross over to the star Cebalrai in Ophiuchus. The Summer Beehive will be nearby.

Date/Time: _____

Location: _____

Weather/Seeing: _____

Notes: _____

_____

Moon Phase:	Sketch:
⊙ ___	

Color added by author

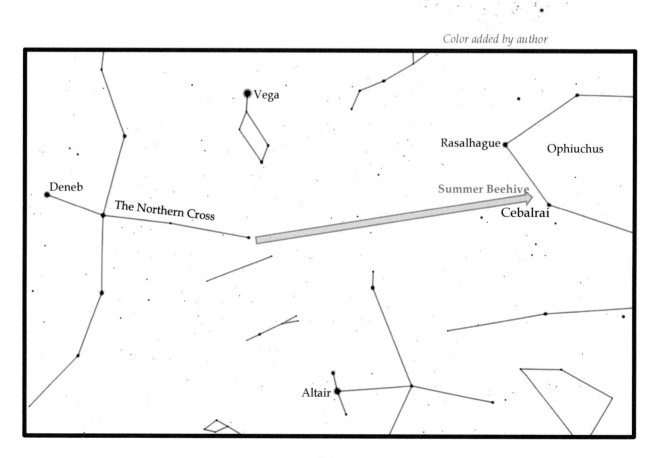

AUTUMN

Sinking slowly below the horizon are Sagittarius and Scorpius, with their glorious deep-sky objects within. The Summer Triangle points down and to the southwest, setting shortly after sunset. If you stay up until midnight in mid-autumn, the constellation Orion peeks his head over the horizon. The Orion Nebula is still too low for evening observation, but it soon will take its place as a primary target in every stargazer's sights.

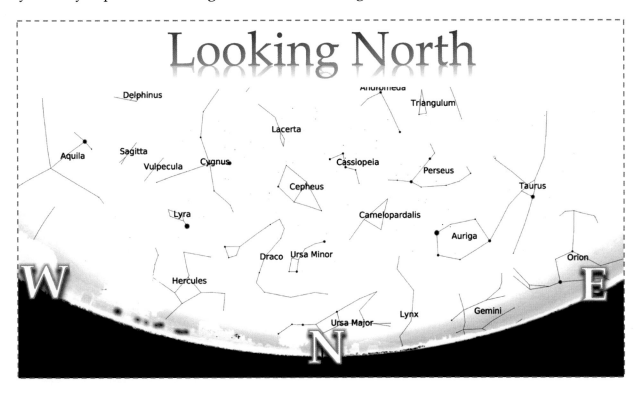

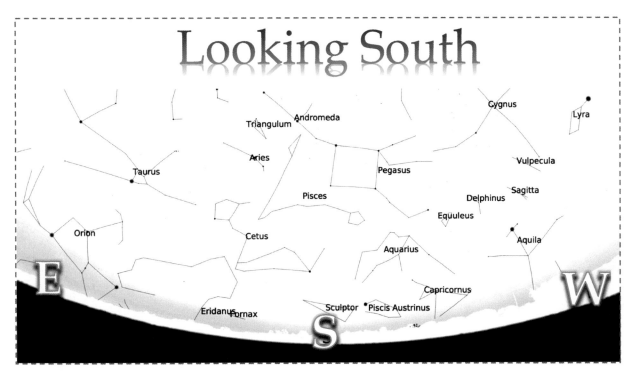

39. Kemble's Cascade

Kemble's Cascade is a beautiful chain of stars located in the northern constellation Camelopardalis. As you pan your scope along this chain of stars, take notice of the star cluster NGC 1502, located at one end of the chain.

Named after Father Lucian Kemble, a Canadian priest whose contributions to amateur astronomy merited his obituary be included in NASA's Astrophysics Data System.[1] Kemble was intrigued by star patterns recognizable in binoculars and mid-sized telescopes (according to his obituary, he owned a Celestron C5). Kemble described this cluster for an article in *Sky and Telescope*. The cluster was later included in the *Millennium Star Atlas*.

These stars are faint, but can be seen with ease in binoculars. In telescopes, use a low magnification eyepiece. Use Cassiopeia (the Big W) as a guide, doubling its length down the top of the W to find Kemble's Cascade.

Date/Time: _____

Location: _____

Weather/Seeing: _____

Notes: _____

_____

Moon Phase: _____   Sketch:

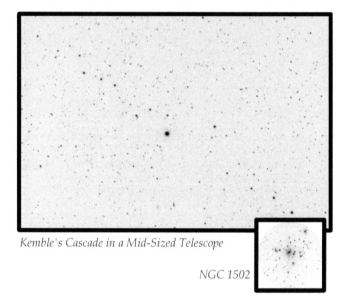

Kemble's Cascade in a Mid-Sized Telescope

NGC 1502

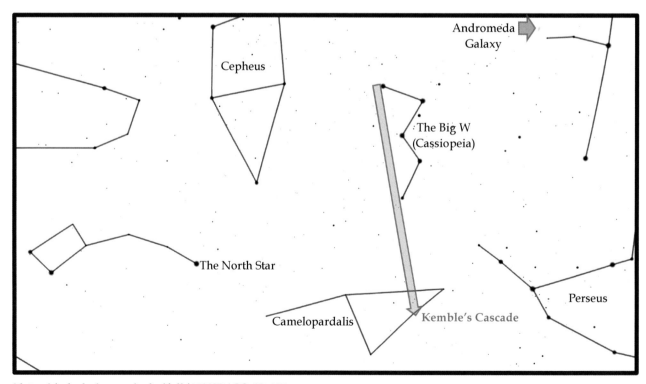

[1] http://adsabs.harvard.edu/full/1999JRASC..93..151

40. The Iris Nebula (Caldwell 4)

The Iris Nebula is a reflection nebula, where a nearby star illuminates interstellar dust.

Though a relatively bright target, the Iris Nebula did not make Charles Messier's list of "items not to be confused with comets." However, an English amateur astronomer, named Sir Patrick Alfred Caldwell-Moore, sought to complement Messier's list with an additional one hundred nine targets he believed most interesting to amateur astronomers. This list is called the Caldwell Catalog. The Iris Nebula is number four on that list. If you have a go-to telescope, the Iris Nebula may be listed as NGC 7023.

To find the Iris Nebula, identify the "square" in the constellation Cepheus. Use the pointer stars in the Big Dipper (low on the autumn horizon) to find the North Star, and then continue that line into Cepheus. Alternatively, use the right arm in Cassiopeia's "W" in the same way. The Iris Nebula is located near the two stars named Alfirk and Alderamin.

Date/Time: _____

Location: _____

Weather/Seeing: _____

Notes: _____

_____

Moon Phase: _____

Sketch:

AUTUMN

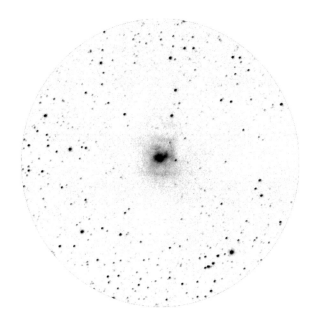

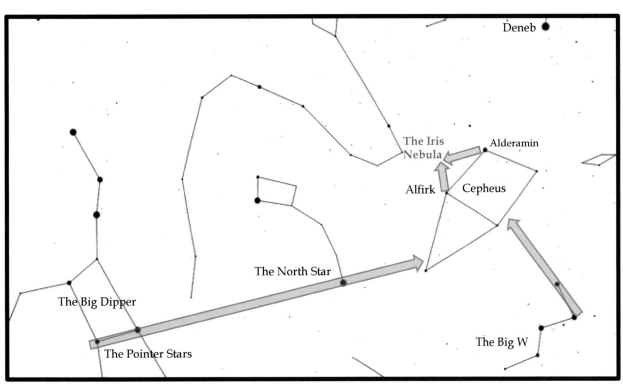

41. Veil Nebula (NGC 6960 and NGC 6992)

Though this nebula is traditionally regarded as one of the more challenging targets for amateur telescopes, improvements in optics have brought it into the realm of the mid-sized telescope. I first saw the Veil Nebula on a dark night on the top of Mount Diablo near San Francisco; the size of the telescope compensating for the light pollution from the nearly five million people living within a hundred-mile radius.

The Veil Nebula is the remains of an exploded star, its debris blowing across our galaxy on invisible interstellar winds. It stretches across the sky at several times the width of the full Moon. Its most visible section (designated NGC 6960) can be found by tracing a line from the top of the Northern Cross through the star on the left arm.

Make sure the Milky Way is glowing bright, to ensure that the sky is dark enough. And use your least powerful eyepiece, as the light from this nebula is spread over a large area. Light pollution filters, or OIII filters, for the eyepiece may also help bring out the details.

Date/Time: _____

Location: _____

Weather/Seeing: _____

Notes: _____

_____

Moon Phase:

Sketch:

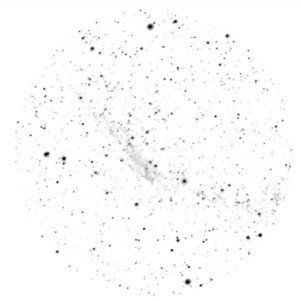

Portion of the Veil Nebula (NGC 6992) as it would appear through a mid-sized telescope under extremely dark skies

MOONLESS NIGHT AND DARK SKY REQUIRED

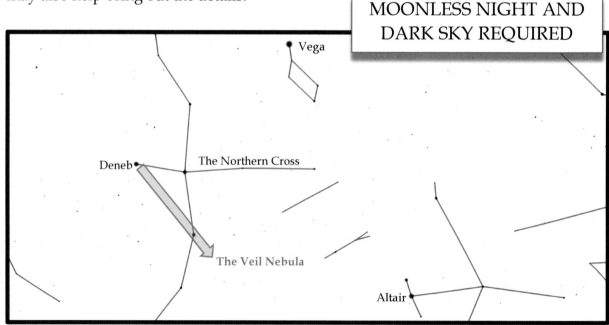

42. M71

This wonderful globular cluster is easy to find, thanks to its location in the pointy shaped cluster Sagitta. Sagitta, or the "Arrow," to me looks like Harry Potter's broom zipping across the sky.

Near the center of the Arrow, like a heart pierced by Cupid, is M71.

This star cluster is only twelve thousand light-years away, which is almost twice as close as the famous "Great Cluster in Hercules." The cluster is bright enough to be seen in light polluted skies and during the full Moon, making it a great target for students at star parties.

To find M71, first locate Sagitta in the Summer Triangle (thanks to this season's lengthening days, the Summer Triangle is visible well into autumn). The cluster is located almost exactly halfway across the constellation, and just slightly below the shaft of the arrow.

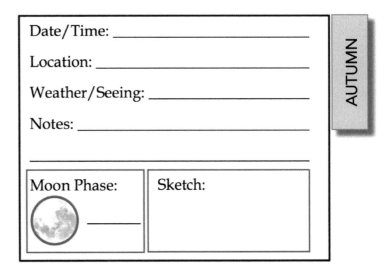

Date/Time: _____

Location: _____

Weather/Seeing: _____

Notes: _____

_____

Moon Phase: _____

Sketch:

AUTUMN

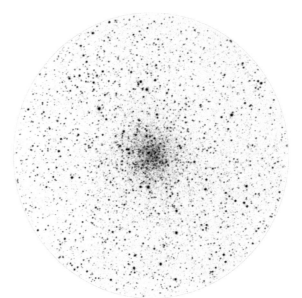

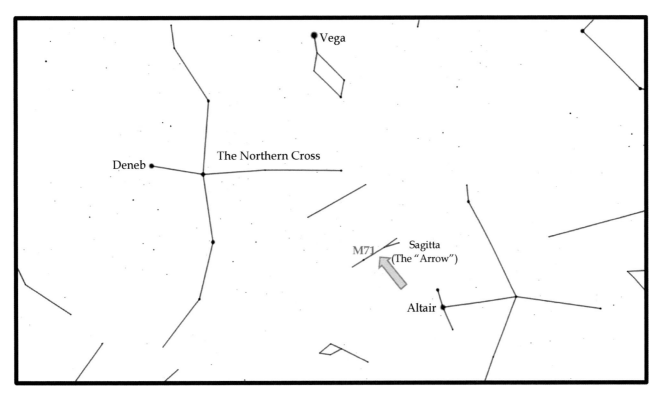

43. Almach (Gamma Andromedae)

I am under special instruction from Steve Jacobs, a longtime member of the Mount Diablo Astronomical Society, to include this wonderful double star in this book.

Almach appears as a bright yellow star right next to a dimmer blue companion. Compare this to Alberio in the Northern Cross, and you can really see the diversity in color.

To find Almach, create a line running from the right arm in the Big W, and follow it over to the next brightest star. While you're in the area, don't forget to check out the Andromeda Galaxy!

If you have a phone adapter, try photographing these bright double stars.

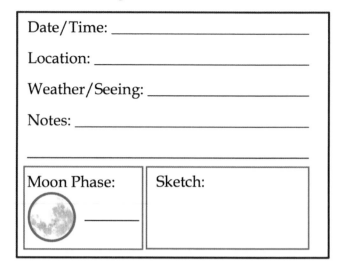

Date/Time: _____

Location: _____

Weather/Seeing: _____

Notes: _____

_____

Moon Phase: _____

Sketch:

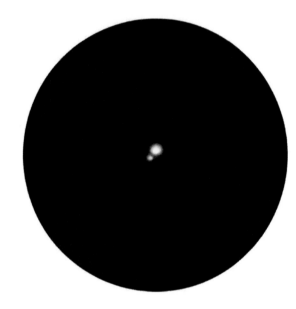

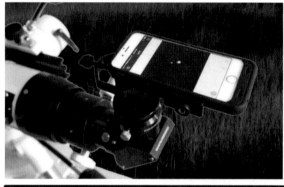

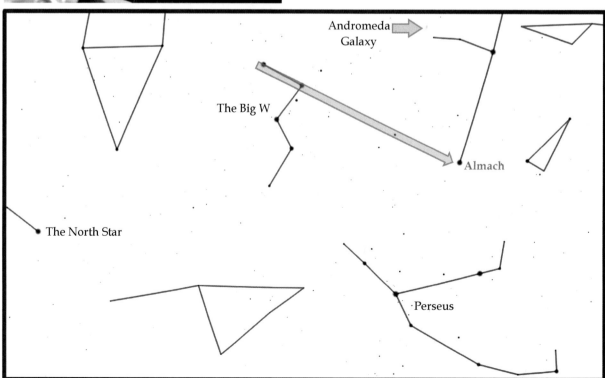

44. E.T. Cluster (NGC 457)

This fantastic open cluster in Cassiopeia used to be primarily known as the "Dragon Fly Cluster" (or the Owl Cluster). But after the Stephen Spielberg classic *E.T. The Extra-Terrestrial* hit theatres in the spring of 1982, this cluster had a colloquial name change, and it's easy to see why.

You have to see this one to believe it. Photographs like the one on the right simply don't capture the effect of two bright eyes, and arms reaching out to grab you!

To find the E.T. Cluster, form a line under the left arm of the Big W (Cassiopeia) and extend it almost, but not quite, directly under the W.

Date/Time: _____

Location: _____

Weather/Seeing: _____

Notes: _____

_____

Moon Phase: _____

Sketch:

AUTUMN

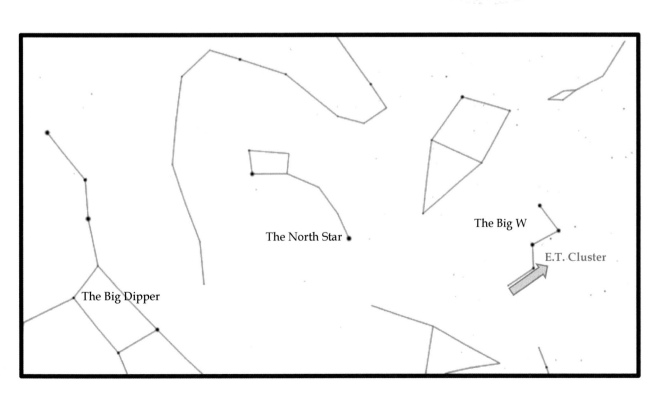

45. The Blue Snowball (NGC 7662)

Here is a dark-sky challenge perfect for the mid-sized telescope. The Snowball is similar to the Ring Nebula, except that a lack of prominent nearby stars makes it more difficult to find.

Some amateur astronomers claim that a six-inch scope is required to see this. However, I was able to pick it up in my four-inch refractor (in perfectly dark skies). In my twelve-inch scope (one that I do not consider mid-sized, for the purpose of this book), I was even able to see the blue coloring!

To find the Blue Snowball, first find Pegasus, a constellation dominated by a giant "box" of stars. Use the Big W (Cassiopeia), and run an imaginary line down to the box, as shown. Form a triangle with the two stars in the top of the box to find the Snowball.

```
MOONLESS NIGHT
RECOMMENDED
```

Date/Time: _____

Location: _____

Weather/Seeing: _____

Notes: _____

_____

Moon Phase: _____   Sketch:

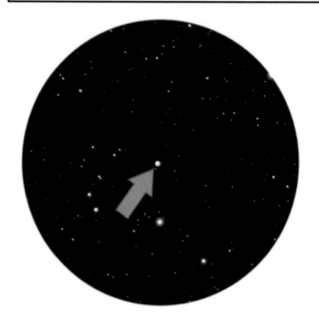

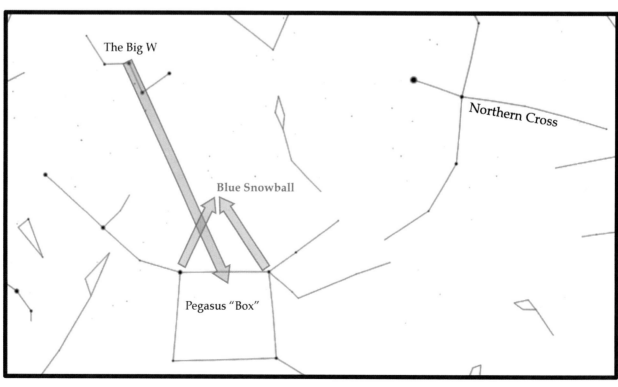

The Big W

Northern Cross

Blue Snowball

Pegasus "Box"

46. M52

This open cluster is worth a look if you are exploring Cassiopeia (the Big W).

M52 was one of French astronomer Charles Messier's original discoveries, when he was still building his catalog of "objects that are not comets", in the year 1774[1].

This cluster is accented by a single bright yellow star, and a dense grouping of stars that seem to form a triangular haze when first viewed at low magnification.

If you want a challenge, right next to M52 lies the bubble nebula, which is visible only in extremely dark skies, in telescopes with diameters eight inches and greater.

To find M52, use the right arm of the Big W, and follow it outward, as shown below. This cluster is dimmer than you may expect, so be sure you adapt your eyes to the dark before attempting the observation.

Date/Time: _____

Location: _____

Weather/Seeing: _____

Notes: _____

_____

Moon Phase: _____

Sketch:

AUTUMN

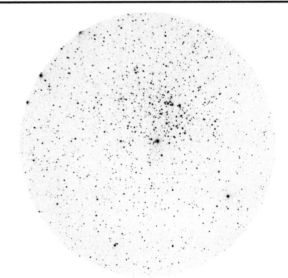

When first viewed at low magnification, the cluster will appear as a triangular haze

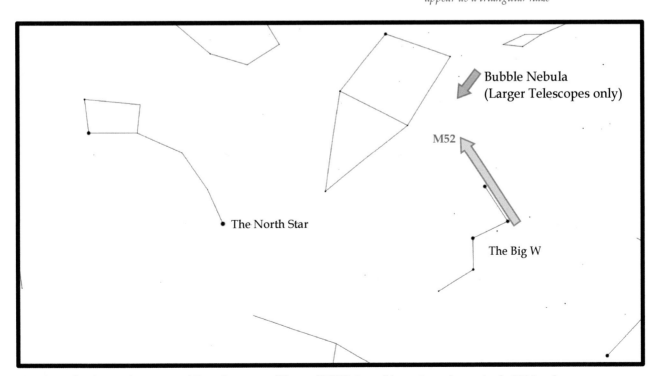

Bubble Nebula
(Larger Telescopes only)

M52

The North Star

The Big W

[1] Students for the Exploration and Development of Space (SEDS): http://messier.seds.org/m/m052.html

47. Triangulum Galaxy (M33)

The Triangulum Galaxy is a spiral galaxy located almost three million light-years from the Milky Way.

M33 is known for its interactions with the Andromeda Galaxy (M31). Astronomers have discovered a bridge of hydrogen and stars extending between M33 and M31, and have determined that these two galaxies collided in the distant past, and will most likely collide again in the future[1].

Using the Big W as a guide, start your search for M33 by finding the Andromeda Galaxy. After you've found the Andromeda Galaxy, notice the two bright stars below it. Follow these stars down to the Triangulum Galaxy.

Don't be concerned if it takes you a while to find it. The last time I observed M33, I was about thirty miles from San Francisco. Despite the moonless nights, and clear skies, finding M33 still took about fifteen minutes.

Date/Time: _____

Location: _____

Weather/Seeing: _____

Notes: _____

_____

Moon Phase:

Sketch:

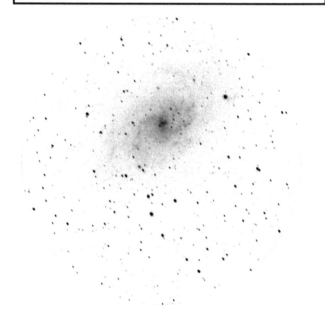

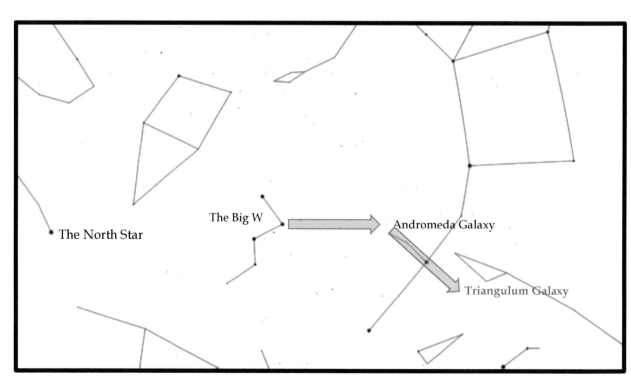

The North Star

The Big W

Andromeda Galaxy

Triangulum Galaxy

[1] The Astrophysical Journal, 751:74 (26pp), 2012 May 20

48. The Spiral Cluster (M34)

M34 is a bright open cluster that makes a great target for light polluted skies, or for when the Moon is bright.

One fun thing to do when observing M34 is to count the double stars within, as many of this cluster's brightest stars are binaries.

Be sure to use your lowest-powered eyepiece. Otherwise, you might not be able to fit the entire cluster into your field of view. Despite the photo to the right, which really doesn't do this cluster justice, the spiral shape is quite defined to the eye.

To find M34, follow Cassiopeia (the Big W) down to identify the two brightest stars in Perseus: Mirphak and Algol. Above Algol is Almaak in Andromeda. You'll find M34 between these two stars.

Date/Time: _____

Location: _____

Weather/Seeing: _____

Notes: _____

_____

Moon Phase: _____

Sketch:

AUTUMN

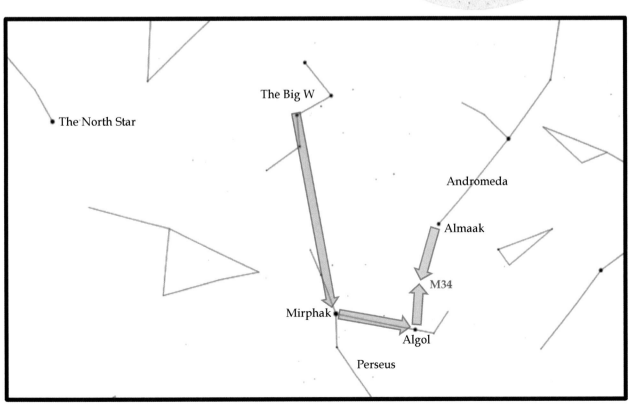

49. M2

Despite being one of our galaxy's largest globular clusters, M2 is often forgotten at star parties due to its awkward location, low in autumn's southern sky. M2 also lacks good reference stars, making it more difficult to find for those (like myself) who rarely use computerized go-to telescopes.

To find M2, use the Summer Triangle, which is just beginning to set in the west. Aquila, the Eagle, should still be visible above the horizon. Use the Eagle's left wing to hop over to the bright star, Sadalsuud in Aquarius. Take note of the other bright star Sadalmelik, and find M2 by forming a triangle with these two stars.

| Date/Time: _____ |
| Location: _____ |
| Weather/Seeing: _____ |
| Notes: _____ |
| _____ |

| Moon Phase: | Sketch: |

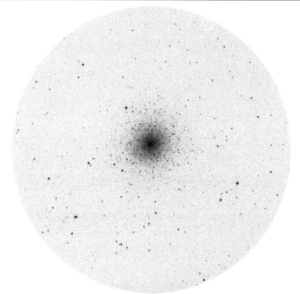

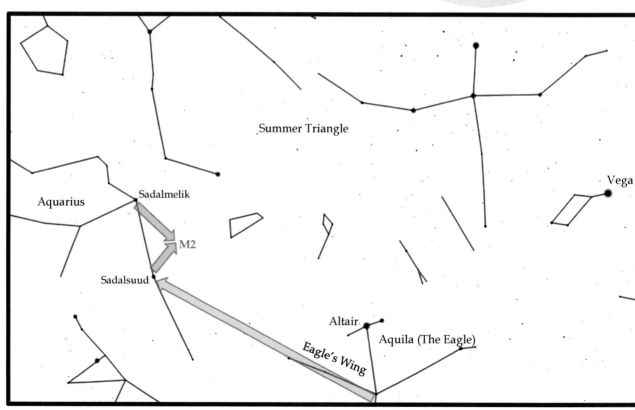

50. Little Scorpion Cluster (NGC 1342)

In *50 Things to See with a Small Telescope*, we looked at the bright star cluster the Pleiades, which looks surprisingly like a little version of the Big Dipper (so much so that many people mistakenly believe the Pleiades *is* the Little Dipper).

About one hand's length from the Pleiades is another miniature version of a larger constellation. NGC 1342, or the Little Scorpion Cluster, bears a striking resemblance to the constellation Scorpius, from the summer sky.

If it's early fall, you should be able to see the Pleiades rising from the eastern horizon (late in the fall, it will be well overhead). To find NGC 1342, use Cassiopeia and the Pleiades to identify two reference stars in Perseus. The little Scorpion is found directly between Algol and the medium-bright star located next to the Pleiades.

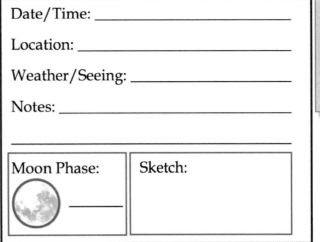

Date/Time: _____

Location: _____

Weather/Seeing: _____

Notes: _____

_____

Moon Phase:

Sketch:

AUTUMN

Dashes added by author

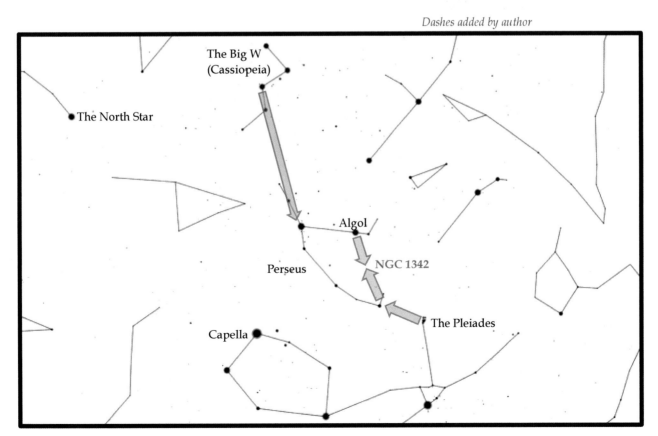

The Big W (Cassiopeia)

The North Star

Algol

NGC 1342

Perseus

The Pleiades

Capella

Appendix – BONUS TARGETS

I spent over a year deciding which targets to include in this book. For each one, I imagined myself at a star party or public outreach event, with a line of kids waiting to see something cool.

As I played this scenario over on the page, targets jumped in and out of the list. Here is a short collection of targets I considered, but eventually cut as I refined each section.

- The Helix Nebula (NGC 7293)
- Ptolemy Cluster (M7)
- 19 Piscium (red star)
- Delta Cephei (variable star)
- T Lyra (red carbon star)
- Porrima (Gamma Virginis)
- The Hyades (large open cluster)
- Keid (Omicron Eridani, triple star)
- Beta Monocerotis (triple star)
- Christmas Tree Cluster (NGC 2264)
- The Demon Star (Algol, Beta Persei)

If this was your first stargazing book and you found it helpful, be sure to consider the prequel, *50 Things to See with a Small Telescope*. The prequel focuses on the very select group of popular targets observed at public star parties all over the world (Northern and Southern Hemisphere editions are available).

63806605R00040

Made in the USA
Middletown, DE
27 August 2019